Inclusive Songs for Resistance & Social Action

Jann Aldredge-Clanton
with composer Larry E. Schultz

Copyright © 2018 by Jann Aldredge-Clanton
Published in the United States of America by Eakin Press
An Imprint of Wild Horse Media Group
P.O. Box 331779
Fort Worth, Texas 76163
1-888-982-8270
www.EakinPress.com
ALL RIGHTS RESERVED
1 2 3 4 5 6 7 8 9

ISBN-10: 1-68179-199-4
ISBN-13: 978-1-68179-199-9
Library of Congress Control Number: 2018952918

CONTENTS

#1-67   **SONGS**

INTRODUCTION

The title of this new collection, *Inclusive Songs for Resistance and Social Action*, comes from our belief that music empowers action for social justice. Music played a large role in the abolition, suffrage, and civil rights movements, and continues to play an important role in the labor movement. Songs also empower other social action movements in our current day. Songs can be a unifying force for social change.

The movement that rose up after the Women's March in January of 2017 inspired many of the songs in this collection. These songs are for use in rallies, marches, and town hall meetings, as well as in faith community worship services.

The Women's March, initiated and led by women, drew people of all genders, races, classes, ages, and abilities. Beginning as a Women's March on Washington, sister marches sprang up in cities in all fifty U.S. states and in more than eighty countries around the world, with an estimated 4.9 million people participating. The Women's March focused on women's rights, while connecting the rights of women to the rights of all races, LGBTQ people, and people of all ages, classes, and abilities. Women's rights are often ignored even in liberation movements, but intersectional feminism emphasizes the vital connection between women's rights and the rights of all people. At the Women's March many of the signs quoted Hillary Rodham Clinton's famous statement at the 1995 Beijing World Conference on Women: "Women's rights are human rights." The 2018 Women's March, also drawing millions of people around the world, continued this focus on the intersection of women's rights and the rights of all people.

President Jimmy Carter in *A Call to Action* asserts that discrimination and violence against women and girls are the world's most serious violations of human rights, and he indicts patriarchal religion as the foundation for this discrimination and violence.[1] Nicholas Kristof and Sheryl WuDunn in *Half the Sky: Turning Oppression into Opportunity for Women Worldwide* lament the "gendercide" resulting from the violence inflicted routinely on women and girls in much of the world, which they call one of the "paramount human rights problems of this century."[2] The "Me Too" movement, created in 2007 by an African American woman named Tarana Burke, went viral on social media in 2017 and underscored the pervasiveness of sexual harassment and assault women around the world suffer. In the United States alone, every nine seconds a woman is battered.[3] An estimated one in three women in the world experiences some kind of abuse in her lifetime;[4] the responses to the "Me Too" movement indicate that estimate may be too low. Worldwide, an estimated four million women and girls each year are bought and sold into prostitution, slavery, or marriage.[5] Seventy percent of the world's poor are women.[6] Exclusively male language for Deity in most worship services and restricting women's leadership form a foundation for this worldwide violence and discrimination against females by devaluing them through exclusion.

This collection centers females, while connecting them to other oppressed groups. Often women experience marginalization and sexism even in social justice movements, as happened in the US civil rights and peace movements of the 1960s and in the more recent Occupy Wall Street movement. Women, socialized to take care of others, often give greater energy to social justice work that benefits other groups more than themselves. While the songs in this collection highlight the intersectionality of justice issues, they place equality and justice for females at the center. Church historian Rev. Dr. Courtney Pace states, "Patriarchy is at the root of every systemic evil, including slavery, racism, sexism, classism, heterosexism, and every other form of oppression."[7] The songs in this collection subvert the foundation of patriarchy through inclusive names and images of the Divine and through celebrating the Divine in biblical and other prophetic women leaders. Women's rights are indeed human rights.

Inclusive Images of Deity

Some people use the term "inclusive" to mean "gender-neutral," but we use it to mean language inclusive of all genders. We also use "expansive" and "gender-balanced" to mean language inclusive of female and male and more. Just as the Black Lives Matter movement has taught us that, though all lives matter, we need to name that black lives matter because they have not mattered enough in our culture, so we need to name females in the divine image, though all genders are all in divine image, because the Female Divine has not been named and valued. We need to name that which has been unnamed, demeaned, devalued, and oppressed.

In this collection we name the Female Divine. Many of the songs feature biblical female names and images of Deity, vital to changing cultures from patriarchal to egalitarian.

In *Inclusive Songs for Resistance and Social Action*, Wisdom is a prominent female personification of the Divine. Our world is in great need of Wisdom, and we need Her guidance to persist in our work of resistance and social action. Wisdom is an ancient divine image, common to many religious traditions. She is *Hokmah* in the Hebrew Scriptures, *Hikmah* in Arabic in the Quran, and *Sophia* in Greek in the Christian Scriptures. Divine Wisdom guides us in our work to bring peace and justice. "Her ways are ways of pleasantness, and all Her paths are peace" (Proverbs 3:17). The song "Wisdom Shows Us Peaceful Pathways" begins with a challenge to include all creation in our transforming work:

> *Wisdom shows us peaceful pathways,*
> *giving hope to keep alive;*
> *joined with Her we go on mission,*
> *helping all creation thrive.*

Some of the songs in this collection draw from the biblical and historical connection between Christ and Wisdom, *Sophia* in the original Greek language of the Christian Scriptures. The Apostle Paul and other biblical writers link *Sophia* and Christ. Paul refers to Christ as "the Wisdom (*Sophia*) of God" (1 Corinthians 1:24), and states that Christ "became for us Wisdom

(*Sophia*) from God" (1 Corinthians 1:30). Proverbs describes Wisdom as the way, the life, and the path (4:11,13,18). The writer of the Gospel of John refers to Christ as "the way, and the truth, and the life" (John 14:6). When we balance the masculine name "Christ" with the feminine name *Sophia* in referring to divinity, we affirm the biblical truth of females and males created equally in the divine image (Genesis 1:27). This equal connection between *Sophia* and "Christ" in our worship supports a community in which all live in partnership. The last stanza of one of the songs prays for guidance to follow Christ-Sophia's way of peace:

> *Come, Christ-Sophia, come today*
> *to show us Your transforming way;*
> *Your wisdom words can still be heard;*
> *we join Your work of peace on earth.*

Another divine name that supports partnership is "Sister-Brother Spirit." We have found "Sister-Brother Spirit" to be an important metaphor for our creative collaboration on this collection and on other hymnbooks and children's music. We believe that Sister-Brother Spirit brought us together and continues to guide our collaboration. "Sister-Brother Spirit" is an inclusive divine name and image, inspiring social justice through shared power. In "We All Dream of Peace and Justice," we sing of joining Sister-Brother Spirit to create a new world, concluding with this stanza:

> *Now we feel the power within us,*
> *and we can make the world anew.*
> *We join with our Sister-Brother Spirit,*
> *giving to all a wider view.*

One of the most powerful biblical female divine names is *Ruah* (Hebrew word for "Spirit"). We find Her in the first chapter of the Bible, giving birth to the universe: "The Spirit (*Ruah*) of God was moving over the face of the waters" (Genesis 1:2) to bring forth light and life. This female Creative Spirit, prominent at the beginning of biblical revelation, has been buried in patriarchal culture and tradition. Resurrecting *Ruah* in our sacred songs will

8

revalue what has been labeled and disparaged as "feminine" and empower us all to embrace the wholeness of our creative gifts. One of the songs in this collection that celebrates the creative power of *Ruah* concludes with this stanza:

> *Ruah, the Spirit, stirs us to grow,*
> *helping to free our creative flow.*
> *She brings us gifts beyond all compare,*
> *new revelations for all to share.*

This collection includes other biblical female names for Deity such as "Mother Eagle," *El Shaddai, Shekhinah,* and "Midwife Divine." As we sing female divine names and images, we affirm the sacred value, dignity, and equality of females in the divine image.

Women Leaders in Scripture

Like the Female Divine, many biblical females have been ignored, excluded, demeaned, misinterpreted, and defamed. Many of the songs in *Inclusive Songs for Resistance and Social Action* reclaim and revalue biblical women. These songs celebrate the power of the Female Divine embodied by biblical women.

Eve is one of the women in Scripture who has been most demeaned and misinterpreted; she has been blamed for sin in the world. The song "Mother Eve Chose Love of Knowledge" reclaims a positive interpretation of Eve, portraying her as a wise woman who embraced the fullness of life and all she was meant to be:

> *Eve, the mother of all living, claimed all she was meant to be;*
> *shining forth in sacred image, she made way for liberty.*
> *Strong and gifted, blessed with Wisdom, Eve engaged her mind and soul,*
> *seeking truth, exploring, naming all creation good and whole.*

This collection also includes songs that highlight often-ignored biblical women, like the Hebrew prophet Huldah. Although we seldom hear about the prophet Huldah in sermons and Bible lessons, she began the biblical canon with her validation of an ancient scroll, probably an early form of the book of Deuteronomy, as the divine word. "Sing a Song of the Prophet

Huldah" celebrates her vital part in biblical history and includes this refrain:

> *Now we will honor the prophet Huldah, singing her story seldom heard;*
> *first to name a book as scripture, she declared the holy Word.*

Several of the songs lament the church's marginalization of biblical women and current women, while also celebrating their resilience and persistence. "And Still We Rise" begins:

> *The women long ignored*
> *still rise from sacred page;*
> *with Wisdom they explored*
> *the truth for every age.*
> *And still they rise,*
> *and still they rise with hope alive,*
> *and still they rise.*

This song then names women leaders in Scripture, like the apostle Junia and the prophet Anna, concluding by connecting overlooked biblical women to current women:

> *Like sisters long ago,*
> *we often are ignored;*
> *still Holy Wisdom shows*
> *us all Her Way to soar.*
> *And still we rise,*
> *and still we rise with hope alive,*
> *and still we rise.*

Many of the largest denominations still refuse to ordain women who are called as ministers. The biblical story of Phoebe confirms that women were ministers in the early church. The song "Deacon Phoebe Claimed Her Calling," based on Romans 16:1-2, includes this stanza questioning why women are still excluded when the Bible clearly records their serving as ministers:

> *Sister Phoebe served as deacon, plain to read in Holy Book.*
> *Why are women then excluded, gifts and graces overlooked?*

The song "The Long-Ignored Disciples" celebrates three women disciples, Mary Magdalene and Joanna and Susanna, who followed Jesus and the other disciples, ministering to them and providing for them (Luke 8:1-3). The song begins with this stanza:

> *The long-ignored disciples illumine Wisdom's way;*
> *their faithful work and witness give guidance for today;*
> *Joanna and Susanna and Mary Magdalene,*
> *these women spread the gospel, providing from their means.*

These songs that celebrate the vital part women played in the biblical story are intended to help spread the Good News of gender justice and equality.

Other Prophetic Women

Inclusive Songs for Resistance and Social Action also features mystic women, like Julian of Norwich and Hildegard of Bingen, and women activists, like Sojourner Truth and Prathia Hall. The songs honor the power of the Female Divine proclaimed and embodied by these prophetic women.

Julian of Norwich (c.1342-c.1416), an anchoress and mystic, proclaims a Christian feminine divinity. Her *Revelations of Divine Love*, based on a series of sixteen visions she received when she was thirty years old, is the first theological book in the English language known to be written by a woman. Julian's vision of the Trinity includes the Female Divine: "God, Almighty, is our kindly Father; and God, All-Wisdom, is our kindly Mother; with the Love and the Goodness of the Holy Ghost, which is all one God."[8] Her visions reveal a Deity who can be called Mother as well as Father: "As verily as God is our Father, so verily God is our Mother."[9] Julian sees the Motherhood of God as threefold: Creator, Sustainer, and Teacher. God gives birth to us; "our precious Mother, Jesus," feeds us "with the Blessed Sacrament that is precious food of very life"; and "Our Gracious Mother" teaches us Her kindness and love.[10]

11

The song "Julian of Norwich Reveals Wisdom's Way" draws from Julian's visions of the Female Divine, illustrated by this stanza:

Julian sees Wisdom, Great Mother of All,
sending us power to take down each wall,
changing the world with Her kindness and grace,
opening all doors for each gender and race.

One of the most influential medieval Christian mystics, Saint Hildegard of Bingen (1098-1179), also uses expansive language for Deity in her prophetic writing and preaching. Drawing from her visions, she celebrates "Holy Wisdom" and other female divine names and images in her work. She describes Wisdom as a powerful female Deity: "Wisdom protects and guides the people who want to follow her, and keeps with great love those who are true to her. Her head shines like lightning, with so much brilliance that you cannot look directly at it. For from the beginning of the world, when Wisdom first openly displayed her workings, she extended in a straight line to the end of time."[11]

In this collection the song "Sister Hildegard Shows the Way" celebrates Hildegard as the embodiment of Holy Wisdom, "guiding all with visions glowing." The first stanza also includes the metaphor "greening power" (*viriditas* in Latin), which Hildegard uses throughout her works to mean spiritual and physical health. In the last stanza of this song Hildegard calls to us with the voice of Holy Wisdom:

Still, Saint Hildegard speaks today,
calling out with Holy Wisdom:
"Follow peaceful, healing ways,
paths of justice, love, and freedom.
All reflect divinity,
joined in mystic harmony."

Sojourner Truth (c.1797-1883), a prominent women's rights activist and abolitionist, embodies Divine Wisdom as she preaches with passion for the liberation of all. Born a slave, Isabella (Belle) Baumfree, she escapes to freedom in 1826 and takes the new name of Sojourner Truth to signify her call to travel and sojourn in various places as she speaks the truth about the sin of slavery.

Also, she is a powerful advocate for women's equal rights. In one of her most famous speeches, delivered at the Ohio Women's Rights Convention in 1851, she proclaims, "If the first woman God ever made was strong enough to turn the world upside down all alone, these women together ought to be able to turn it back, and get it right side up again! And now they are asking to do it, the men better let them."[12] Sojourner Truth's legacy of feminism and racial equality still resonates today.

The song "Sojourner Truth Came to Set People Free" rejoices in her visionary work for racial and gender justice, beginning with this stanza:

> *Sojourner Truth came to set people free,*
> *claiming her vision of full liberty,*
> *freeing the slaves held by gender and race,*
> *guiding us all to create a new place.*

Rev. Dr. Prathia Hall (1940-2002), civil rights movement leader and womanist theologian, also embodies the Female Divine. Courageous in civil rights activism, she was arrested many times, shot at, wounded, and jailed for weeks. She preached with such power that Dr. Martin Luther King Jr. once remarked, "Prathia Hall is one platform speaker I prefer not to follow."[13] She was one of the first African American women ordained by the American Baptist Churches USA. Active in the Student Nonviolent Coordinating Committee (SNCC), she was head of the Selma Project and the Atlanta Project, training many Northern white college students. Overcoming many obstacles, "she worked tirelessly for justice" and "transformed her suffering into prophetic proclamation." Prathia Hall "turned ashes into beautiful breaths of life."[14]

Prathia Hall's repetition of "I have a dream" in a public prayer inspired Martin Luther King Jr.'s famous speech. The first stanza of the song "Prathia Hall Spoke Up" gives her credit:

> *Prathia Hall spoke up, and people then woke up*
> *to take a stand;*
> *she was the first to say, "I have a dream today,"*
> *showing the freedom way,*
> *the promised land.*

13

The last stanza celebrates her also as a womanist scholar teaching "Wisdom's Word" of racial and gender equality.

The prophetic women celebrated in the songs in this collection proclaim Wisdom's truth and lead people on Her paths of peace and justice.

Resistance Songs for Rallies and Marches

Songs empower social justice movements. This collection includes songs to use in rallies, marches, and other activist gatherings to support movements such as Women's March, Equity for Women in the Church, Black Lives Matter, Human Rights Campaign, Poor People's Campaign, and GreenFaith: Interfaith Partners for the Environment.

Many of these songs draw inspiration from women's rights activism. "She Persisted Still" celebrates women, like Madame Curie, who have persevered to overcome obstacles of sexism:

> *Madame Curie found the cures to many ills,*
> *yet they tried to question her scientific skills;*
> *nevertheless, she persisted boldly;*
> *she persisted still.*

The song "'Time's Up,' We Shout!" focuses on the "Me Too" and "Time's Up" movements to stop sexual assault and harassment, and begins with this stanza:

> *We are tired of abuse, exploitation, misuse,*
> *so we join in the movement "Me Too";*
> *breaking silence, we shout and together speak out,*
> *claiming voices with power anew.*

"We All Rise Up for Human Rights," one of the songs emphasizing the connection between women's rights and all human rights, includes this stanza:

> *We all rise up for women's rights for equal pay and power,*
> *for women's rights are human rights for all to fully flower.*

This song collection highlights the intersectionality of sexism, racism, heterosexism, classism, and other social justice concerns. For as Martin Luther King Jr. declared, "Injustice anywhere is a threat to justice everywhere."[15]

Equity for Women in the Church is an ecumenical movement working for justice and equality for all races and genders. The mission of this movement is to facilitate equal representation of clergywomen as pastors of multicultural churches in order to transform church and society. Included in this collection are songs that bring race and gender together in our work for equity, illustrated by this stanza in "The Spirit Dwells Within Us All":

> We now rise up for equity,
> for race and gender rights;
> we work to set all people free
> from all oppressive plights.

The song "When People Follow Wisdom's Way," celebrating the power of Divine Wisdom to bring liberation through gender and racial justice, includes this stanza:

> When racial justice comes on earth, She will set us free;
> then all will know each other's worth; She will set us free.

Class intersects with race and gender in our work to overcome injustices. Workers' rights activism inspires some of these songs. "Join Now All Together" highlights the vital role faith plays in supporting labor movements, illustrated by this concluding stanza:

> Faith and labor joining, singing truth to power,
> we bring transformation in this urgent hour.
> Greedy empires topple; everyone will thrive,
> claiming all our talents, keeping hope alive.

The refrain calls faith communities to come together with others to advocate for workers' rights:

> Join now all together; everyone unite,
> marching on for justice, for all workers' rights.

Ecofeminism and ecowomanism teach us that environmental justice intersects with gender, racial, and economic justice. References to the earth are traditionally feminine, but the feminine is not given sacred value in our worship. Like females, the earth suffers exploitation, assault, and abuse. People of color, especially women, and economically disadvantaged people suffer disproportionately from environmental crises. Many songs in this collection support caring for the environment through female divine names and images, connecting the revaluing of females to the revaluing of the earth. For example, in "El Shaddai Will Hold Us Fast" we sing of "joining Her" to "nurture Earth." "We Will All Resist" includes this stanza:

> *Care of Earth will never ever be denied;*
> *care of Earth will never ever be denied,*
> *for we will rise up stronger all together;*
> *we will all resist.*

Some of the songs, like "We Will All Resist," bring together gender, racial, economic, environmental, and other justice concerns, calling us to rise up and take action.

Advent and Christmas Carols

Discovering a widespread longing for inclusive lyrics to familiar Christmas tunes, we have published many songs for Advent and Christmas celebrations.[16] These carols have struck a chord with many faith communities and have become some of our most popular works. A CD, *Sing of Peace*,[17] consists of ten of these songs, and another CD, *Inclusive Hymns for Liberating Christians*,[18] includes several Advent and Christmas songs.

Just when we think we have published songs to all the Christmas tunes we love, we discover more. This collection includes more Advent and Christmas carols to tunes such as GOD REST YOU MERRY, I WONDER, FRENCH CAROL, and COVENTRY CAROL.

We hope that these new carols and all the songs in this new collection will inspire communities and individuals to join in the creation of inclusive worship. *Inclusive Songs for Resistance and Social Action* comes to you with the invitation to empower your justice and peace movements with music.

NOTES

1. Jimmy Carter, *A Call to Action* (New York: Simon & Schuster, 2014).

2. Nicholas D. Kristof and Sheryl WuDunn, *Half the Sky: Turning Oppression into Opportunity for Women Worldwide* (New York: Knopf, 2009), xiii, xvii.

3. "Every 9 Seconds in the US a Woman Is Assaulted or Beaten - Help End Domestic Violence," PRWEB (Austin, TX: October 8, 2012), http://www.prweb.com/releases/2012/10/prweb9986276.html.

4. United Nations General Assembly, "In-Depth Study on All Forms of Violence against Women: Report of the Secretary General, 2006," A/61/122/Add.1.6 (July 2006), www.un.org/en/women/endviolence/pdf/VAW.pdf.

5. The United Nations Population Fund, The State of World Population 2000 report, "Lives Together, Worlds Apart: Men and Women in a Time of Change" (2000), http://www.unfpa.org/swp/2000/english/ch03.html.

6. Louise Arbour, "Despite human rights treaties, low-intensity discrimination against women is rampant," *thestar.com* (March 8, 2008), https://www.thestar.com/opinion/2008/03/08/despite_human_rights_treaties_lowintensity_discrimination_against_women_is_rampant.html. "International Women's Day: Laws and 'Low Intensity' Discrimination against Women" (March 8, 2008).

7. Courtney Pace, "Subversive Sisters: A Herstory of Our Foremothers," *Nevertheless She Preached* (Waco, TX: September 21, 2017), https://www.youtube.com/watch?v=7qBeqG5HOPk&t=38s&index=6&list=PLihMSf5UsFiCzjESH6ruX6EpTpLopLZQt.

8. Julian of Norwich, *Revelations of Divine Love*, ed. Dom Roger Hudleston (London: Burns & Oates, 1927), 119.

9. Ibid., 121.

10. Ibid., 123-31.

11. Hildegard of Bingen, *Scivias*, trans. Mother Columba Hart and Jane Bishop (New York: Paulist Press, 1990), 465-66.

12. Sojourner Truth, "Ain't I a Woman?" speech, quoted in *Modern History SourceBook* (August 1997),

https://sourcebooks.fordham.edu/mod/sojtruth-woman.asp.

13. Martin Luther King Jr., quoted in "Tough Platform Speaker Dr. Martin Luther King Preferred Not to Follow," by Jae Jones, *Black Then: Discovering Our History* (December 1, 2017),

https://blackthen.com/prathia-hall-tough-platform-speaker-dr-martin-luther-king-preferred-not-to-follow/.

14. Courtney Pace, "Prathia Hall: An Extraordinary, Ordinary Saint," *ETHICSDAILY.com* (August 28, 2014),

http://www.ethicsdaily.com/prathia-hall-an-extraordinary-ordinary-saint-cms-22090.

15. Martin Luther King Jr., "Letter from Birmingham Jail" (April 16, 1963), in *Why We Can't Wait* (New York: Penguin Books, 1964), 77.

16. Jann Aldredge-Clanton with composer Larry E. Schultz, *Inclusive Hymns for Liberating Christians* (Austin, TX: Eakin Press, 2006); *Inclusive Hymns for Liberation, Peace, and Justice* (Austin, TX: Eakin Press, 2011); *Earth Transformed with Music: Inclusive Songs for Worship* (Fort Worth, TX: Eakin Press, 2015).

17. Devi Vaani and Jann Aldredge-Clanton, *Sing of Peace* (Occidental, CA: Joe Hoffmann Studios, 2015).

18. Jann Aldredge-Clanton with composer Larry E. Schultz, *Inclusive Hymns for Liberating Christians CD*, performed by congregation, choirs & orchestra of Pullen Memorial Baptist Church, Raleigh, North Carolina (Pinehurst, NC: Ward Productions, 2007).

1 All Together We Have Power

Isaiah 58:12

All to-geth-er we have pow-er, ris-ing up a-gainst all the wrong; all to-geth-er we have pow-er, ris-ing up to sing free-dom songs.

Words: Jann Aldredge-Clanton
Music: African-American spiritual; arr. Larry E. Schultz.

FEEL THE SPIRIT
Irregular

1. The Spir - it in us feels so strong,
2. When we are sti - fled and op - pressed,
3. When things a - round us don't feel right,
4. The Spir - it in all brings new birth,

D.C. al Fine

giv - ing us hope to la - bor long.
we will all share our deep dis - tress.
we will re - sist with all our might.
mov - ing with love through all the earth.

2   And Still We Rise

"Still I Rise," Maya Angelou; Luke 1:46-55, 2:36-38, 8:1-3; Acts 18:24-27; Romans 16:1-2,7; Proverbs 3:17

1. The wom - en long ig - nored still rise from sa - cred page;
2. The wom - en preached the Word; the Bi - ble makes it clear;
3. The proph - et An - na sees her vi - sion come to light,
4. A - pos - tle Jun - ia leads, and Dea - con Phoe - be prays;
5. Like sis - ters long a - go, we of - ten are ig - nored;

with Wis - dom they ex - plored the truth for ev - ery age.
still man - y have not heard these sis - ters through the years.
and Moth - er Mar - y frees op - pressed from pain - ful plight.
Jo - an - na does good deeds; Pris - cil - la shows the Way.
still Ho - ly Wis - dom shows us all Her Way to soar.

Refrains 1-4: And still they rise, and still they rise with
Refrain 5: And still we rise, and still we rise with

hope a - live, and still they rise.
hope a - live, and still we rise.

Words: Jann Aldredge-Clanton
Music: John Darwall
Words © 2016 Jann Aldredge-Clanton.

DARWALL
6.6.6.6.8.8

Apostle Junia Rises

Romans 16:7

1. A - pos - tle Jun - ia ris - es and spreads the gos - pel truth, em -
2. A - pos - tle Jun - ia ris - es to claim her right - ful place, though
3. A - pos - tle Jun - ia ris - es with Wis - dom for our day; we

bod - ies Ho - ly Wis - dom, gives res - ur - rec - tion proof; a
of - ten dis - re - gard - ed, ex - clud - ed, and e - rased; some
join her in per - sist - ing till jus - tice comes to stay; pro -

strong and faith - ful lead - er, she helps the move - ment thrive; im -
change her name in Scrip - ture to try to make her male; they
claim - ing life a - bun - dant, we make the Good News heard, and

pris - oned for her bold - ness, she keeps her hope a - live.
fol - low sex - ist cus - toms, but Jun - ia still pre - vails.
o - pen doors of wel - come, give wit - ness to the Word.

Words: Jann Aldredge-Clanton
Music: English melody; arr. Ralph Vaughan Williams
Words © 2017 Jann Aldredge-Clanton.

KING'S LYNN
7.6.7.6 D

4 As We Come to the Table of Love

Mark 12:31

1. What is re - quired to come to this ta - ble?
2. Liv - ing as one, we join 'round this ta - ble.

Who is al - lowed to share in its feast?
Giv - ing to all, we of - fer its feast.

There is no lim - it, no hin - drance, no bound - ary.
Ev - er em - brac - ing, and nev - er re - ject - ing,

No one is la - beled "most hon - ored" or "least."
we keep this ta - ble a ta - ble of peace.

Words and Music: Nancy E. Petty & Larry E. Schultz
Words and Music © 2017 Nancy E. Petty & Larry E. Schultz.

TABLE OF LOVE
Irregular

5 Bravely the Hebrew Midwives Spoke Up

Exodus 1:15-22

1. Brave - ly the He - brew mid-wives spoke up, thwart-ing the e - vil
2. Bold - ly the mid-wives fol-lowed Wis - dom, sav - ing the He - brew
3. Mid - wife Di - vine filled them with pow - er, giv - ing them strength to

Pha - raoh's plans; Pu - ah and Shi - phrah wise - ly woke up,
ba - by boys; Pu - ah and Shi - phrah claimed their free - dom
stand for life; Pu - ah and Shi phrah did not cow - er;

tak - ing the pow - er from his hands. These fear - less wom - en
from all of Pha - raoh's wick - ed ploys. They dis - re - gard - ed
they showed a way for end - ing strife. With them we rise to

saved their race, act - ing with cour - age, faith, and grace.
his com - mands, chose to re - sist un - just de - mands.
chal - lenge wrong, keep - ing our faith and cour - age strong.

Words: Jann Aldredge-Clanton
Music: Georg Neumark
Words © 2017 Jann Aldredge-Clanton.

NEUMARK
9.8.9.8.8.8

Celebrate Sister Lydia's Vision

6

Acts 16:13-15, 40; Galatians 5:1

1. Cel - e - brate Sis - ter Lyd - i - a's vi - sion; she ful - fills her life - giv - ing
2. Ev - ery race, ev - ery gen - der is wel - come, all af - firmed in Lyd - i - a's
3. We will join Sis - ter Lyd - i - a's mis - sion, form - ing cir - cles, o - pen and

call; she fol - lows So - phi - a Wis - dom, cre - at - ing a place for
home, first church to be formed in Eu - rope, dis - ci - ples who spread sha-
free; as e - qual cre - a - tive part - ners, we birth new com - mu - ni-

all, cre - at - ing a place for all.
lom, dis - ci - ples who spread sha - lom.
ty, we birth new com - mu - ni - ty.

All have free - dom to blos - som ful - ly in a cir - cle of hope and peace;

the Good News reach - es to ev - ery - one, as jus - tice and love in - crease.

Words: Jann Aldredge-Clanton
Music: H. Ernest Nichol
Words © 2016 Jann Aldredge-Clanton.

MESSAGE
10.8.8.7.7 with refrain

7   Celebrate the Prophet Deborah

Judges 4:1-5, 5:1-12

1. Cel - e - brate the proph - et Deb - orah, her brave sto - ry now re - claim;
2. Hok - mah Wis - dom raised up Deb - orah as the judge in all the land;
3. Deb - orah spoke the Word of Hok - mah, help - ing all be free and fair.

Deb - orah led the He - brew peo - ple, bring - ing hon - or to her name.
peo - ple came to her for guid - ance, seek - ing jus - tice from her hand.
Like the judge and proph - et Deb - orah, we can rise up an - y - where.

Now a - wake! Sing of Deb - orah. Now a - wake; sing of Deb - orah, wise and

strong. Cel - e - brate her sto - ry! Now join in sing - ing Deb - orah's song.

(Deb - orah's song.)

Words: Jann Aldredge-Clanton
Music: Emily D. Wilson
Words © 2018 Jann Aldredge-Clanton.

HEAVEN
8.7.8.7. with refrain

Come, Christ-Sophia, Come, We Pray

Proverbs 3:13-18; 1 Corinthians 1:24

1. Come, Christ - So - phi - a, come, we pray; we
2. Our world is filled with deep dis - tress; we
3. Come, Christ - So - phi - a, give us grace to
4. We keep our hope a - live and well; our
5. Come, Christ - So - phi - a, come to - day to

need Your Ad - vent here to - day; we
hear the cries of all op - pressed; though
wel - come and af - firm each race; we
jus - tice mis - sion will not fail, for
show us Your trans - form - ing way; Your

long to see all peo - ple free to
hate as - sails we still pre - vail, and
hear Your call, in - clud - ing all, and
love is strong, wins o - ver wrong; we
wis - dom words can still be heard; we

join Your work of peace on earth.

Words: Jann Aldredge-Clanton
Music: John Baptiste Calkin

WALTHAM
8.8.8.8 (LM)

Words © 2016 Jann Aldredge-Clanton.

9 Come, Gather Now in Circles

Proverbs 1:20-23, 3:17, 8:1-23; Wisdom 7:27

Come, gath-er now in cir - cles; gath-er the peo-ple ev - ery - where;

come, gath-er now in cir - cles, So - phi - a's peace to share.

1. So - phi - a Wis-dom preach - es Her truth from age to age; She
2. How long must Wis-dom cry out be - fore in - jus - tice fails? Though
3. So - phi - a Wis-dom calls us to join Her work of peace, to

sends Her ur - gent mes-sage through proph - et and through sage.
scoffed and scorned She la - bors till lov - ing care pre - vails.
fol - low paths of jus - tice, Her right - eous-ness in - crease.

Words: Jann Aldredge-Clanton
Music: African-American spiritual
Words © 2017 Jann Aldredge-Clanton.

GO TELL IT
7.6.7.6 with refrain

Come, Join Our Movement Now

Come, join our move-ment now, ris-ing up to set us all free;

Fine

come, join our move-ment now, work-ing hard for change we can see.

1. We're ris-ing so wom-en will all have full rights,
2. We're ris-ing so jus-tice will come for each race, ris-ing up to set us all free;
3. We're ris-ing so work-ers will all have fair pay,
4. We're ris-ing to-geth-er for hu-man rights now,

D.C. al Fine

we work for jus-tice now with all our might,
the Spir-it gives us en-er-gy and grace,
we join to-geth-er bring-ing a new day, work-ing hard for change we can see.
the Spir-it moves in us to show us how,

Words: Jann Aldredge-Clanton
Music: African-American spiritual
Words © 2017 Jann Aldredge-Clanton.

SWING LOW
Irregular

11

Come, Mother Eagle

Deuteronomy 32:11-12; Isaiah 40:31

1. Come, Moth-er Ea-gle, when our hearts grow wea-ry; take us a-loft on Your em-pow-ering wings; show us Your high-er vi-sion now more clear-ly, that we can make a world where free-dom rings.

2. When we are tired of ris-ing and re-sist-ing, come, Moth-er Ea-gle, give us strength a-new; lift us up high with hope to keep per-sist-ing till all the world can share Your jus-tice view.

3. Come, Moth-er Ea-gle, help us keep on grow-ing, join-ing with You to reach up to the sky, that we cre-ate a world of kind-ness flow-ing, where ev-ery-one can free-ly learn to fly.

Come, Moth-er Ea-gle, teach us to soar, spread-ing your bless-ings of peace for-ev-er-more.

Words: Jann Aldredge-Clanton
Music: James Walch
Words © 2018 Jann Aldredge-Clanton.

TIDINGS
11.10.11.10 with refrain

Come, Ruah, Breath of Life

Genesis 1:1-2; Acts 2:1-18

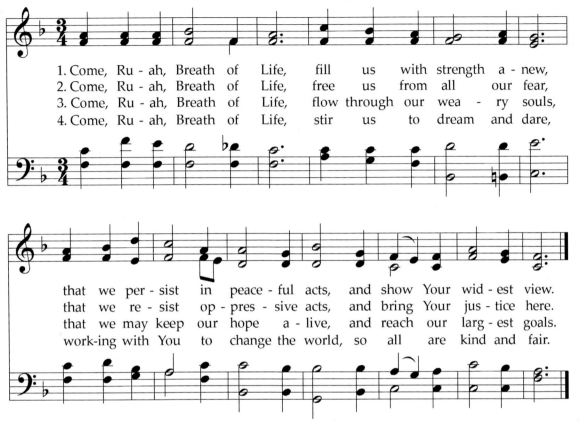

1. Come, Ru - ah, Breath of Life, fill us with strength a - new,
2. Come, Ru - ah, Breath of Life, free us from all our fear,
3. Come, Ru - ah, Breath of Life, flow through our wea - ry souls,
4. Come, Ru - ah, Breath of Life, stir us to dream and dare,

that we per - sist in peace - ful acts, and show Your wid - est view.
that we re - sist op - pres - sive acts, and bring Your jus - tice here.
that we may keep our hope a - live, and reach our larg - est goals.
work-ing with You to change the world, so all are kind and fair.

Words: Jann Aldredge-Clanton
Music: Robert Jackson
Words © 2017 Jann Aldredge-Clanton.

TRENTHAM
6.6.8.6 (SM)

13   Deacon Phoebe Claimed Her Calling

Romans 16:1-2

1. Dea-con Phoe-be claimed her call-ing, liv-ened by the Spir-it's flow;
2. Dea-con Phoe-be took Paul's let-ter to the ear-ly church in Rome;
3. Sis-ter Phoe-be served as dea-con, plain to read in Ho-ly Book.
4. We will rise like Dea-con Phoe-be, claim-ing Ho-ly Spir-it's call,

faith-ful min-is-ter and lead-er, Phoe-be helped the church to grow.
she sup-port-ed man-y oth-ers, o-pened wide her heart and home.
Why are wom-en then ex-clud-ed, gifts and grac-es o-ver-looked?
spread-ing lib-er-at-ing gos-pel that in-cludes and wel-comes all.

Words: Jann Aldredge-Clanton
Music: Lizzie Tourjée
Words © 2017 Jann Aldredge-Clanton.

WELLESLEY
8.7.8.7

El Shaddai Will Hold Us Fast

14

Genesis 49:25; Isaiah 43:2

1. El Shad-dai will hold us fast, guid-ing through each storm-y blast; when the tem - pest round us rolls, She will calm our anx - ious souls, giv - ing com - fort, hope, and grace, lift - ing all in Her em - brace.

2. When our work is hard and long, El Shad - dai will keep us strong, giv - ing cour - age to per - sist, strength to rise up and re - sist; She will help us face our fear, keep - ing dreams and vi - sions clear.

3. El Shad - dai will bring new life, help - ing ev - ery - one to thrive; blessed by Her cre - a - tive flow, all will free - ly, ful - ly grow; join - ing Her, we nur - ture Earth, fill - ing hearts with love and mirth.

Words: Jann Aldredge-Clanton
Music: John E. Gould
Words © 2018 Jann Aldredge-Clanton.

PILOT
7.7.7.7.7.7

15 Follow Wisdom

Proverbs 3:17-18

Fol - low Wis-dom; She keeps our spir - its grow-ing; fol - low Wis-dom; She will guide us on path-ways in-to free-dom. Join all to-geth-er now; fol-low Wis - dom's way, Her peace - ful way where love holds sway. Oh,

Words: Jann Aldredge-Clanton
Music: African-American spiritual
Words © 2017 Jann Aldredge-Clanton.

DEEP RIVER
Irregular

Harriet Tubman Leads to the Promised Land 16

Exodus 6:2-8; Luke 4:18-19

1. When Har - riet Tub - man leads the way,
2. The Spir - it gives her faith and power,
3. When Har - riet Tub - man helps those bound, set - ting peo - ple free;
4. With Spir - it strong she risks her life,
5. Like Har - riet Tub - man we will rise,

they call her Mo - ses of that day,
she ris - es in that ur - gent hour,
they flee by Rail - road Un - der - ground, set - ting peo - ple free.
she helps the slaves es - cape the strife,
like her we will be brave and wise,

Har - riet Tub - man leads to the prom - ised land;

we will join her, set - ting peo - ple free.

Words: Jann Aldredge-Clanton
Music: African-American spiritual
Words © 2017 Jann Aldredge-Clanton.

GO DOWN MOSES
Irregular

17   Heal Our World, O Christ-Sophia

Proverbs 3:17-18; Revelation 21:5

1. Heal our world, O Christ-So-phi - a; heal us all, we pray;
2. Hear the ur - gent cries of chil-dren, march-ing for their lives;
3. Wom-en rise up now for jus - tice, call - ing out "Me Too";
4. Help us join Your work of heal-ing, that we all may thrive;

fill us all with lov - ing kind - ness; show Your peace - ful way.
help us now to end the vio - lence, so they all sur - vive.
Black Lives Mat - ter move-ment joins in mak - ing all things new.
give us grace and strength for ac - tion; keep our hope a - live;

Christ - So - phi - a, heal our world, we pray;

fill us all with lov - ing kind - ness; show Your peace - ful way.

Words: Jann Aldredge-Clanton
Music: W. Howard Doane
Words © 2018 Jann Aldredge-Clanton.

PASS ME NOT
8.5.8.5 with refrain

Hear Our Cries, Sophia

Proverbs 1:20-23; Psalm 92:7

18

Hear our cries, hear our cries, hear our cries, So - phi - a;
hear our cries, hear and a - rise; hear and a - rise, So - phi - a.

1. You cry out with us; you feel in - jus - tice with us.
2. Come, give us cour - age when e - vil - do - ers flour - ish;
3. Come, give us wis - dom to work with you for free - dom;

How long, how long will wrong pre - vail? Hear and a - rise, So - phi - a.
with you we all will o - ver - come; hear and a - rise, So - phi - a.
with you we will cre - ate new life; hear and a - rise, So - phi - a.

Words: Jann Aldredge-Clanton
Music: African-American spiritual
Words © 2017 Jann Aldredge-Clanton.

STEAL AWAY
5.7.8.7 with refrain

19 Join Now All Together

1. Join now all to-geth - er; ev-ery-one u - nite, march-ing on for jus - tice, for all work-ers' rights; call for liv-ing wag - es, tak-ing down each wall, safe and fair con - di - tions, ben - e - fits for all. Join now all to-geth - er; ev-ery-one u - nite, march-ing on for jus - tice, for all work-ers' rights.

2. Faith and la-bor join - ing, sing-ing truth to power, we bring trans-for-ma-tion in this ur - gent hour. Greed-y em-pires top - ple; ev-ery-one will thrive claim-ing all our tal - ents, keep-ing hope a - live.

Words: Jann Aldredge-Clanton
Music: Arthur Sullivan
Words © 2015 Jann Aldredge-Clanton.

ST. GERTRUDE
6.5.6.5 D with refrain

Join Together, Sisters, Brothers

Genesis 1:1-2; Galatians 5:22; 2 Timothy 1:7

1. Join to-geth-er, sis-ters, broth-ers; let us work to end the strife; ris-ing up with one an-oth-er, we will la-bor long for life. Ru-ah Spir-it, Great Cre-a-tor, moves in us to help all thrive.

2. Rise to end a-buse and vio-lence; Ru-ah joins our work for right; e-vil can-not ev-er si-lence voic-es raised a-gainst the blight. Speak-ing out to end in-jus-tice, we re-sist with all our might.

3. Ru-ah Spir-it gives us pow-er to cre-ate the world a-new; join-ing Her, we ful-ly flow-er, var-ied forms and var-ied hues. Come, u-nite in peace-ful ac-tion, giv-ing all Her hope-ful view.

Words: Jann Aldredge-Clanton
Music: Mark Andrews
Words © 2017 Jann Aldredge-Clanton.

LAUDA ANIMA (Andrews)
8.7.8.7.8.7

21 Join with the Spirit

Genesis 1:1-2; 2 Timothy 1:7

Swing (♩♩ = ♪♪)

Join with the Spir-it; join with the Spir-it, ris-ing;

Ru - ah, Ru - ah,

Fine

join with the Spir-it; She will em-pow-er our ris-ing.

Ru - ah, Ru - ah,

1. See those wom-en's rights de-nied,
2. See the im - mi - grants a - bused,
3. Work for ra - cial jus - tice now;
4. We will hold each oth - er fast;

She will em-pow-er our ris-ing;

by
their
all
some

Oo...

D.C. al Fine

lead - ers who have of - ten lied;
ba - sic hu - man rights re - fused;
those op-pressed will show us how;
day we will be free at last;

She will em - pow-er our ris-ing.

Oo...

Words: Jann Aldredge-Clanton

Music: African-American spiritual; arr. Larry E. Schultz

WADE

7.8.8.8 with refrain

Julian of Norwich Reveals Wisdom's Way 22

Proverbs 3:13-18, 4:8-9

1. Jul - ian of Nor - wich re - veals Wis - dom's way,
2. Jul - ian sees Wis - dom, Great Moth - er of All,
3. Now Sis - ter Jul - ian in - spires us to grow,
4. Still Sis - ter Jul - ian re - veals mys - tic dreams,

show - ing us vi - sions for our cur - rent day,
send - ing us pow - er to take down each wall,
reach - ing our full - ness of cre - a - tive flow;
well - springs of heal - ing from Earth's sa - cred streams.

vi - sions of love bring - ing all in - to one,
chang - ing the world with Her kind - ness and grace,
joined with So - phi - a, our Wis - dom and Friend,
All shall be well, and all things shall be well;

beau - ty from dawn - ing to set - ting of sun.
open - ing all doors for each gen - der and race.
we claim our whole - ness, our life with - out end.
jus - tice and peace shall for - ev - er pre - vail.

Words: Jann Aldredge-Clanton
Music: Traditional Irish melody
Words © 2017 Jann Aldredge-Clanton.

SLANE
10.10.10.10

23   Longing for a Peaceful Day

Proverbs 3:17

1. When our path is hard and long, Wis-dom helps to keep us strong;
2. Sis - ters, broth-ers, hand in hand, we will take a jus - tice stand,
3. Ho - ly Wis-dom brings new life; She will help to end the strife.

Refrain: **Long - ing for a peace - ful day, we have gath-ered here to pray;**

She in - spires a hope-ful song, giv-ing power to o - ver-come wrong.
joined with those in ev - ery land, seek-ing peace for all hand in hand.
All our dreams and hopes re-vive, as we join Her la - bor for life.

Ho - ly Wis-dom guides our way, deep with - in us al-ways will stay.

Words: Jann Aldredge-Clanton
Music: Traditional North American hymn
Words © 2015 Jann Aldredge-Clanton.

CLOSER WALK
7.7.7.8

Longing for Her Rebirth

24

Proverbs 1:20-23, 3:17-18

1. Our wea - ry world in an - guish cries, long - ing for
2. When will Her peace and love in - crease? When will all
3. For ag - es long So - phi - a's song rings out through
4. Wis - dom So - phi - a helps us see ev - ery - one's

Her re - birth; we yearn to bring So -
know Her worth? So - phi - a yearns to
all the earth; we seek to - day Her
sa - cred worth; with voic - es strong we

phi - a nigh, long - ing for Her re - birth.
help us learn Wis - dom for Her re - birth.
peace - ful way, long - ing for Her re - birth.
sing Her song, long - ing for Her re - birth.

Words: Jann Aldredge-Clanton
Music: *Pageant of the Shearmen and Taylors*, 15th cent.
Words © 2017 Jann Aldredge-Clanton.

COVENTRY CAROL
8.6.8.6 (CM)

25   Marching for Liberty

1. Gon-na come join the move - ment,
2. Gon-na come join for wom-en's rights,
3. Gon-na come join for work-ers' rights,
4. Gon-na come join with ev - ery race, marching for lib-er-ty

march - ing for lib-er - ty, march - ing for lib-er - ty;

gon - na come join the move - ment,
gon - na come join for wom - en's rights,
gon - na come join for work - ers' rights,
gon - na come join with ev - ery race, march-ing for lib-er-ty, gon-na

set all peo - ple free.   We're gon-na

Words: Jann Aldredge-Clanton
Music: African-American spiritual
Words © 2017 Jann Aldredge-Clanton.

STUDY WAR NO MORE
Irregular

26 Mother Eve Chose Love of Knowledge

Genesis 1-3

1. Moth - er Eve chose love of knowl - edge,
2. Eve, the moth - er of all liv - ing,
3. If Eve on - ly knew the dam - age

trust - ing Wis - dom deep with - in;
claimed all she was meant to be;
done to wom - en in her name,

long have man - y twist - ed Scrip - ture,
shin - ing forth in sa - cred im - age,
she would rise with all her cour - age,

slan - dered Eve, blamed her for sin.
she made way for lib - er - ty.
gen - der jus - tice to pro - claim.

Words: Jann Aldredge-Clanton
Music: Thomas John Williams
Words © 2017 Jann Aldredge-Clanton.

EBENEZER
8.7.8.7 D

Though ma - ligned, she still will flour - ish,
Strong and gift - ed, blessed with Wis - dom,
Stirred by her in - trep - id spir - it,

mov - ing out from E - den's bower;
Eve en - gaged her mind and soul,
we will seize this ur - gent hour;

we re - store her an - cient sto - ry,
seek - ing truth, ex - plor - ing, nam - ing
guid - ed by our in - ner Wis - dom,

praise her life - af - firm - ing power.
all cre - a - tion good and whole.
we like Eve speak truth to power.

27 Now the Spirit Comes

Habakkuk 2:2-3; John 8:32; Revelation 21:5

1. When the storm clouds round us gath-er, Bless-ed Spir-it comes to cheer
2. When in-jus-tice o-ver-pow-ers, we u-nite a-gainst the wrong,
3. We will join hands, bring-ing heal-ing, o-pening doors of lib-er-ty;
4. With our vi-sions bright-ly beam-ing, we cre-ate the world a-new;

She will calm all rag-ing weath-er, cast-ing out our doubt and fear.
and the Spir-it free-ly show-ers gifts of hope to keep us strong.
and the Spir-it keeps re-veal-ing truth to set all peo-ple free.
and the Spir-it keeps us dream-ing, giv-ing all Her glo-rious view.

Now the Spir-it comes, bless-ing ev-ery-one; She will sure-ly hold us fast;

keep-ing hope a-live, She will help us thrive, so we all are free at last.

Words: Jann Aldredge-Clanton
Music: W. S. Marshall
Words © 2017 Jann Aldredge-Clanton.

BLESSED QUIETNESS
8.7.8.7 with refrain

Our Hearts Cry Out in Longing

Proverbs 3:17; Luke 4:18; 1 Corinthians 1:24

Unison

1. Our hearts cry out in long-ing for jus-tice and peace. Oh,
2. We la-bor bring-ing Wis-dom So-phi-a to birth, to
3. Re-joice now for the Good News is com-ing to stay, for

when will op-pres-sion and vio-lence all cease? Oh,
give us the pow-er to make peace on earth; with
Wis-dom So-phi-a is born on this day; She

when will the cap-tives all find full re-lease? Our
Her all cre-a-tion re-claims sa-cred worth; we
guides us to-geth-er on Her peace-ful way; re-

hearts cry out in long-ing for jus-tice and peace.
la-bor bring-ing Wis-dom So-phi-a to birth.
joice now for the Good News is com-ing to stay.

Words: Jann Aldredge-Clanton
Music: Appalachian melody, arr. Larry E. Schultz

I WONDER
12.11.11.12

29 Prathia Hall Spoke Up

Proverbs 2:9-10, 3:13-18, 4:8-9

1. Pra - thi - a Hall spoke up, and peo - ple then woke up
2. Lead - er of civ - il rights, Pra - thi - a Hall shed light
3. Pro - phet - ic preach - er bold, Pra - thi - a Hall took hold
4. Wom - an - ist schol - ar too, Pra - thi - a Hall held true

to take a stand; she was the first to say,
on jus - tice ways; her free - dom faith pre - vailed
of Wis - dom's power; she o - pened doors for all
to Wis - dom's Word; she taught e - qual - i - ty,

"I have a dream to - day," show - ing the
e - ven when she was jailed; though wound - ed
to claim our gos - pel call, break - ing op -
gen - ders and rac - es freed to be all

free - dom way, the prom - ised land.
and as - sailed, she still held sway.
pres - sive walls, so gifts may flower.
we can be, all voic - es heard.

Words: Jann Aldredge-Clanton
Music: *Thesaurus Musicus*, 1744

AMERICA
6.6.4.6.6.6.4

Queen Esther Saved Her People

Esther 4-8

1. Queen Es - ther saved her peo - ple; she helped them all sur - vive;
2. Queen Es - ther moved with cour - age in that most ur - gent hour;
3. Queen Es - ther met each chal - lenge with - in her time and place;
4. In such a time as this now we work for sav - ing life;

she risked her life to save them, to keep them all a - live.
for such a time she came to the seat of roy - al power.
she faced op - pres - sion based on her gen - der and her race.
we speak a - gainst in - jus - tice and act to end the strife.

When vio - lent forc - es gath - ered, she heed - ed Wis-dom's voice,
In spite of fear of dan - ger, she spoke life - giv - ing words,
For such a time she rose up and fol - lowed Wis-dom's ways,
With Es - ther we claim cour - age to rise up and re - sist;

and stood up for her peo - ple to make the lov - ing choice.
and joined with Ho - ly Wis - dom to make her mes - sage heard.
re - sist - ing e - vil ac - tions, cre - at - ing bet - ter days.
with her we find our pow - er and pa - tience to per - sist.

Words: Jann Aldredge-Clanton
Music: Welsh hymn melody; *Hymnau a Thonau*, 1865
Words © 2017 Jann Aldredge-Clanton.

LLANGLOFFAN
7.6.7.6 D

31 Radiant Mother

inspired by Aramaic versions Matthew 6:9-13; Luke 11:2-4

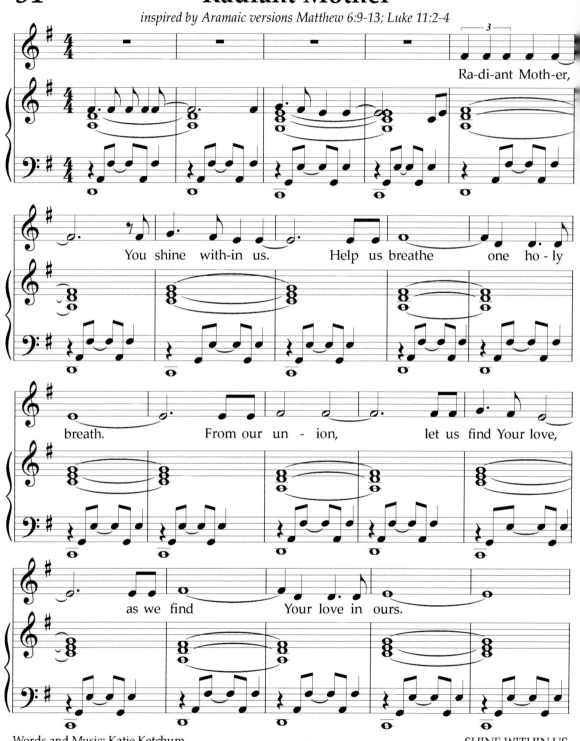

Ra-di-ant Moth-er, You shine with-in us. Help us breathe one ho-ly breath. From our un-ion, let us find Your love, as we find Your love in ours.

Words and Music: Katie Ketchum
Words and Music © 2016 Katie Ketchum.

SHINE WITHIN US
Irregular

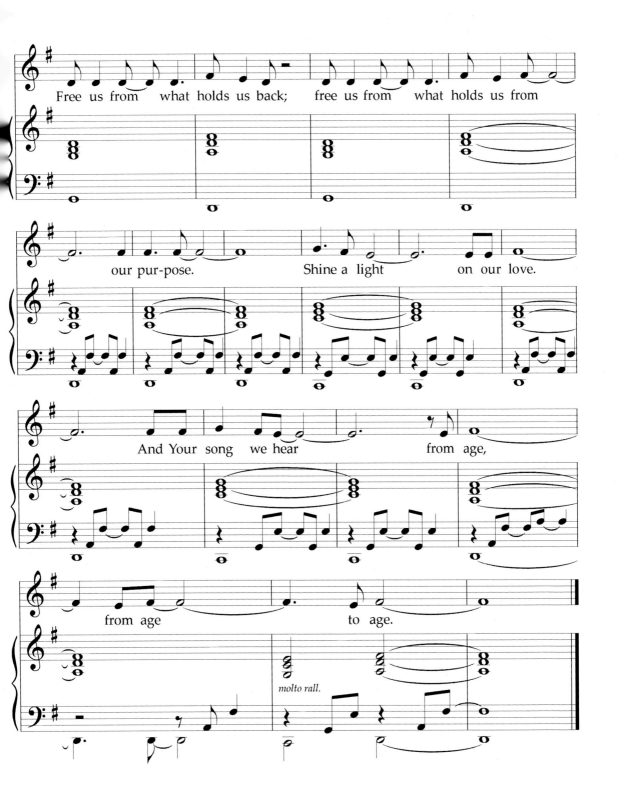

32 Rise, Sisters, Brothers, Rise

Isaiah 58:12

1. Rise, sisters; rise, brothers; rise, sisters, brothers, rise.
2. We'll be marching; we'll be marching; we'll be marching for our rights.
3. We'll be singing; we'll be singing; we'll be singing for our rights.
4. We'll be calling; we'll be calling; we'll be calling for our rights.
5. We'll be voting; we'll be voting; we'll be voting for our rights.
6. Rise, sisters; rise, brothers; rise, sisters, brothers, rise.

If we all rise up today, we create a better way, and the Spirit of freedom will rise.

Words: Jann Aldredge-Clanton
Music: African-American spiritual; arr. Larry E. Schultz
Words © 2017 Jann Aldredge-Clanton; Music arr. © 2018 Larry E. Schultz.

O FREEDOM
Irregular

Rise Up for Justice

Refrain: We will all rise up for jus - tice; we will
1. We rise up for rights of wom - en; we rise
2. We rise up for ra - cial jus - tice; we rise
3. We rise up for gen - der jus - tice; we rise
4. We rise up for rights of work - ers; we rise
5. We rise up for rights to health - care; we rise

all rise up for jus - tice; we will all rise up for
up for rights of wom - en; we rise up for rights of
up for ra - cial jus - tice; we rise up for ra - cial
up for gen - der jus - tice; we rise up for gen - der
up for rights of work - ers; we rise up for rights of
up for rights to health - care; we rise up for rights to

jus - tice; u - nit - ed we will stand.
wom - en; u - nit - ed we will stand.
jus - tice; u - nit - ed we will stand.
jus - tice; u - nit - ed we will stand.
work - ers; u - nit - ed we will stand.
health-care; u - nit - ed we will stand.

Words: Jann Aldredge-Clanton
Music: Traditional
Words © 2017 Jann Aldredge-Clanton.

OLD TIME RELIGION
Irregular

34 Rosa Parks Made Way for Freedom

Acts 1:8

1. Ro - sa Parks made way for free - dom, lead - ing work for civ - il rights
2. Moth - er of the free - dom move - ment, Ro - sa Parks in - spired re - forms
3. Ro - sa Parks brought lib - er - a - tion, chang - ing his - tory on that bus;

she re - sist - ed seg - re - ga - tion, helped re - move this sin - ful blight.
peo - ple fol - lowed her brave ac - tion, chang - ing rac - ist laws and norms.
her strong mor - al cour - age led to bet - ter life for all of us.

On a bus in Al - a - bam - a, she sat down and took a stand,
With the Ho - ly Spir - it's pow - er, she drew guid - ance from the Word,
With the Spir - it liv - ing in her, she per - sist - ed; she held fast;

claim - ing e - qual rights and ac - cess, e - qual jus - tice in our land.
work - ing side by side with oth - ers, so all voic - es could be heard.
we will fol - low her brave ac - tion, till we all are free at last.

Words: Jann Aldredge-Clanton
Music: William Moore's *Columbian Harmony*, 1825
Words © 2017 Jann Aldredge-Clanton.

HOLY MANNA
8.7.8.7 D

Roses & Birds

1. Go to Her with your an - ger. Go to Her with your doubt.
2. Go to Her when you've lost all hope. Go to Her when you need a friend.

Go to Her when you're full of fear. Go to Her in con - fu - sion. And
Go to Her with grat - i - tude. Go to Her with a lov - ing heart.

She will give you ros - es, and She will give you birds that sing. And She will give you the

deep - est love She brings. brings.

Words and Music: Katie Ketchum
Words and Music © 2016 Katie Ketchum.

GUADALUPE
Irregular

36 Ruah, the Spirit, Breathes in Our Souls

Deuteronomy 10:19; Luke 10:27-37; Romans 12:13

1. Ru - ah, the Spir - it, breathes in our souls, giv - ing us
2. When we have la - bored with no suc - cess, Ru - ah, the
3. Ru - ah, the Spir - it, keeps hope a - live, fill - ing our
4. Ru - ah, the Spir - it, stirs us to grow, help - ing to

vi - sions, chal - leng - ing goals. She guides us all to o - pen new
Spir - it, feels our dis - tress. She gives us strength to rise a - gainst
hearts with cour - age to thrive. She gives us grace to weath - er each
free our cre - a - tive flow. She brings us gifts be - yond all com -

doors, wel - come all stran - gers, neigh - bors, and more.
wrong, speak up for those who suf - fer so long.
storm, join Her in work to heal and trans - form.
pare, new rev - e - la - tions for all to share.

Words: Jann Aldredge-Clanton
Music: George C. Stebbins
Words © 2017 Jann Aldredge-Clanton.

ADELAIDE
5.4.5.4 D

Sacred Spark of Life and Beauty

Psalm 133:1; Galatians 5:22

37

Unison

1. Sa - cred spark of life and beau - ty, God - dess Brig - id
2. Sa - cred well of lov - ing kind - ness, Moth - er Brig - id
3. Sa - cred queen of earth and heav - en, Sis - ter Brig - id

brings new birth, spring-ing forth in fields of flow - ers,
pours out care, eas - ing all our pain and sor - row,
bless - es all, bring-ing ev - ery - one to - geth - er,

giv - ing hope to all on earth; while in - spir - ing verse and
bring-ing heal - ing ev - ery - where; spring of Wis - dom ev - er
tak - ing down di - vid - ing walls; peace and u - ni - ty will

mu - sic, she will fill our hearts with mirth.
flow - ing, she will guide us all to share.
flour - ish as we fol - low her clear call.

Words: Jann Aldredge-Clanton
Music: Traditional French carol
Words © 2016 Jann Aldredge-Clanton.

PICARDY
8.7.8.7.8.7

38 She Persisted Still

Exodus 15:20-21; Micah 6:4; Mark 16:9-11; Luke 18:2-8; 2 Timothy 4:2

Refrain

She per-sist-ed, she per-sist-ed still; she per-sist-ed, she per-sist-ed still;

nev-er-the-less, she per-sist-ed bold-ly; she per-sist-ed still. *(Fine)*

Stanzas (additional stanzas on opposite page)

1. Mir - i - am the proph - et led the Is-rael-ites; she got lit-tle praise for
2. Mar - y Mag-da - lene gave wit-ness to the Word, yet they tried to keep her
3. So - journ-er Truth claimed her pro-phet-ic voice, yet they tried to squelch her,

(D.C. al Fine)

her part in the flight; nev-er-the-less, she per-sist-ed bold-ly; she per-sist-ed still.
voice from be-ing heard; nev-er-the-less, she per-sist-ed bold-ly; she per-sist-ed still.
take a-way her choice; nev-er-the-less, she per-sist-ed bold-ly; she per-sist-ed still.

Words: Jann Aldredge-Clanton
Music: African-American spiritual
Words © 2017 Jann Aldredge-Clanton.

I SHALL NOT BE MOVED
Irregular

She Persisted Still
Additional Stanzas

4. Madame Curie found the cures to many ills,
   yet they tried to question her scientific skills;
   nevertheless, she persisted boldly;
   she persisted still.

5. Prathia Hall preached truth with all her power,
   yet they tried to stop her in the crucial hour;
   nevertheless, she persisted boldly;
   she persisted still.

6. Katherine Johnson's figures launched us into space,
   yet they undermined her gender and her race;
   nevertheless, she persisted boldly;
   she persisted still.

39

She Sets Us Free

John 8:32; Galatians 5:22, 25

1. All are long-ing for the day when there is peace on earth;
2. Day by day the Spir-it's hand touch-es our deep-est pain;
3. Now we claim our sa-cred worth; now we can dream and dare,

gath-ered here we join to pray, hop-ing to bring re-birth.
ev-ery-where Her love ex-pands, free-ing from cus-tom's chains.
join-ing hands, trans-form-ing earth, blos-som-ing ev-ery-where.

Feel the Spir-it in our hearts, keep-ing our hope a-live;
She af-firms and bless-es all, heal-ing from hate and strife;
Praise the Spir-it in our souls, giv-ing us lib-er-ty;

with the pow-er She im-parts, we all can thrive.
joined with Her we take down walls and bring new life.
with Her truth the world is whole and all are free.

Words: Jann Aldredge-Clanton
Music: Howard E. Smith
Words © 2016 Jann Aldredge-Clanton.

SAFETY
7.6.7.6.7.6.7.4 with refrain

She   sets   us   free!   She   sets   us   free!
(sets   us free!)   (sets   us free!)

Fol - low the Spir-it's call;   She sets us free.   She   sets us free!

40 She Will Rise

Words: Stacy Boorn
Music: Katie Ketchum; arr. Larry E. Schultz

HERFESTIVAL
Irregular

Shekhinah Shines Throughout the World 41

Exodus 40:34-38, 29:45; Habakkuk 2:2-3

1. She - khi - nah shines through - out the world; Her
2. She - khi - nah guides through wil - der - ness, where
3. She - khi - nah sends us en - er - gy to
4. She - khi - nah is our prom - ised home; in

glo - ry fills all lands; She leads to paths of
ev - ery dream seems lost; She gives us strength to
rise a - gainst the wrong; She helps us all to
Her we safe - ly dwell; She wel - comes ev - ery -

jus - tice - love; Her vi - sion still ex - pands.
car - ry on, no mat - ter what the cost.
o - ver - come, and lifts our hearts with song.
one with love; for - ev - er all is well.

Words: Jann Aldredge-Clanton
Music: African-American spiritual; arr. Harry T. Burleigh
Words © 2018 Jann Aldredge-Clanton.

McKEE
8.6.8.6 (CM)

42   Sing a Song of the Prophet Huldah

2 Kings 22:13-20; 2 Chronicles 34:22-33

1. Sing a song of the proph-et Hul-dah, lift-ing up her voice of power
2. Hok-mah Wis-dom guid-ed Hul-dah, speak-ing bold-ly with-out fear;
3. Now re-claim the wom-en proph-ets, ris-ing up from sa-cred page;

she be-gan the ho-ly can-on; sa-cred Word with Hul-dah flowere
king and priests con-sult-ed Hul-dah, claimed her words for all to hear.
fol-low Hul-dah and all proph-ets, speak-ing truth from age to age.

Now we will hon-or the proph-et Hul-dah, sing-ing her sto-ry sel-dom heard;

first to name a book as Scrip-ture, she de-clared the ho-ly Word.

Words: Jann Aldredge-Clanton
Music: W. Walker's *Southern Harmony*, 1835
Words © 2016 Jann Aldredge-Clanton.

RESTORATION
8.7.8.7 with refrain

Sing of Holy Wisdom

Proverbs 3:13-18, 4:8-13; Luke 11:49

43

1. Sing of Holy Wisdom; bring Her truth to birth;
2. Holy Wisdom comes through prophets' voices raised,
3. Holy Wisdom welcomes true diversity;
4. Holy Wisdom heals us, nurtures and uplifts;

cel - e - brate Her Advent; praise Her sacred worth.
born in all who seek Her just and loving ways.
dark and light enhance Her creativity.
come, let us adore Her; claim Her glorious gifts.

She comes to give us peaceful ways to live.

Sing of Holy Wisdom; bring Her truth to birth.

Words: Jann Aldredge-Clanton
Music: Traditional French carol
Words © 2017 Jann Aldredge-Clanton.

NOEL NOUVELET
6.5.6.5 with refrain

44 Sister Hildegard Shows the Way

Proverbs 1:20-23, 3:17-18

1. Sis - ter Hil - de - gard shows the way, guid - ing all with
2. Moth - er Hil - de - gard gives new life, open - ing all con-
3. Po - et Hil - de - gard sings of Love, ev - er - last - ing,
4. Still, Saint Hil - de - gard speaks to - day, call - ing out with

vi - sions glow - ing, mir - a - cles of heal - ing rays,
fin - ing plac - es, lead - ing us to end the strife,
ev - er - giv - ing, deep with - in us and a - bove,
Ho - ly Wis - dom: "Fol - low peace - ful, heal - ing ways,

lov - ing - kind - ness ev - er - grow - ing. Dai - ly she in-
re - cre - at - ing peace - ful spac - es. Joined in cir - cles,
streams of beau - ty ev - er - liv - ing. Join - ing her cre-
paths of jus - tice, love, and free - dom. All re - flect di-

spires re - birth, green - ing pow - er fill - ing earth.
free and fair, we will spread her lov - ing care.
a - tive song, all are blessed, trans - formed, and strong.
vin - i - ty, joined in mys - tic har - mo - ny."

Words: Jann Aldredge-Clanton
Music: *Allgemeines Katholisches Gesangbuch*, ca. 1774
Words © 2016 Jann Aldredge-Clanton.

GROSSER GOTT
8.8.7.8.7.7

Sojourner Truth Came to Set People Free 45

Proverbs 3:13-18, 4:10-27

Unison

1. So - journ - er Truth came to set peo - ple free,
2. So - journ - er Truth sang a Spir - it - filled song,
3. So - journ - er Truth preached to take down each wall,
4. So - journ - er Truth led the way to new life,

claim - ing her vi - sion of full lib - er - ty,
plead - ing for peo - ple who suf - fered so long:
o - pen - ing doors to new free - dom for all,
chal - leng - ing e - vil so peo - ple can thrive;

free - ing the slaves held by gen - der and race,
"Rise up and act so all rights are re - stored;
help - ing her race to es - cape pain - ful plights,
with her we fol - low the Wis - dom and Way,

guid - ing us all to cre - ate a new place.
help those who la - bor with - out a re - ward."
as she urged wom - en to claim e - qual rights.
work - ing for jus - tice and peace to hold sway.

Words: Jann Aldredge-Clanton
Music: Traditional Irish melody
Words © 2017 Jann Aldredge-Clanton.

SLANE
10.10.10.10

46 Sophia Friend

Proverbs 3:13-18, 7:4

1. So-phi-a Friend hears ev-ery prayer; She comes to free us from de-spair; Her lov-ing voice calms ev-ery fear with words of com-fort al-ways near. She comes through dark-ness and through light; we feel Her heal-ing day and night; to-geth-er now we sing this song, our hope and cour-age grow-ing strong.

2. So-phi-a Friend hears ev-ery prayer; She comes with ten-der lov-ing care; we call on Her through pain and grief; She comes to bring us all re-lief. We feel Her gen-tle, kind em-brace, Her touch of peace, Her touch of grace; re-stored and blessed, we find new life; our bod-ies, minds, and spir-its thrive.

3. So-phi-a Friend hears ev-ery prayer; She comes to help us dream and dare; Her pres-ence in us ev-ery day will guide us on Her peace-ful way. Her pow-er sets all peo-ple free to be all we are meant to be; we now re-claim our sa-cred worth, and cel-e-brate with all on earth.

Words: Brian Burton & Jann Aldredge-Clanton
Music: William B. Bradbury
Words © 2015 Brian Burton & Jann Aldredge-Clanton.

SWEET HOUR
8.8.8.8 D (LMD)

Sophia, Holy Wisdom

Proverbs 3:17-18

47

1. So - phi - a, Holy Wis - dom, be born in us, we pray;
2. Now vio - lence and op - pres - sion bring suf - fering ev - ery - where;
3. Your Ad - vent, Ho - ly Wis - dom, brings Good News un - to all;
4. So - phi - a, Ho - ly Wis - dom, we cel - e - brate Your birth;

we la - bor for Your com - ing, Your just and peace - ful way;
come, live in us, So - phi - a, and stir us all to dare,
You give us all new pow - er to take down ev - ery wall,
You bring new hope of free - dom and peace through - out the earth;

our wound - ed world cries out to You for heal - ing ev - ery day:
to join with You to change the world, to spread Your lov - ing care:
so ev - ery gen - der, ev - ery race can feel Your sa - cred call:
now ev - ery - one and all cre - a - tion claim our sa - cred worth:

So - phi - a, our wis - dom and peace, wis - dom and peace;

So - phi - a, our wis - dom and peace!

Words: Jann Aldredge-Clanton
Music: *Little Book of Christmas Carols*, ca. 1850   Words © 2014 Jann Aldredge-Clanton.

GOD REST YOU MERRY
7.6.7.6.8.6 with refrain

48 Sophia, Waiting for Your Light

Proverbs 3:13-18; Genesis 1:2; Acts 2:1-4

Words: Katie Ketchum, Jann Aldredge-Clanton & Larry E. Schultz
Music: African-American spiritual; arr. Katie Ketchum & Larry E. Schultz
Words © 2017 Katie Ketchum, Jann Aldredge-Clanton & Larry E. Schultz.
Music arr. © 2018 Katie Ketchum & Larry E. Schultz.

WONDERFUL CHILD
Irregular

*Alternate refrain texts: *Sophia* ("Wisdom") is suitable
for Advent and *Ruah* ("Breath/Spirit") for Pentecost.

fill us with Your wis-dom, all of Your glo-rious free-dom. We
bring Your pre-cious treas-ure, gifts be-yond ev-ery mea-sure. You

cel-e-brate Your an-cient sto-ry, and claim your won-drous love and glo-ry. We
are a Tree of Life and liv-ing, a Source of joy for-ev-er giv-ing. Your

long to see Your re-birth; we are wait-ing for Your peace on earth, to
hope with-in us will grow; we are wait-ing for the world to know Your

see all peo-ple join-ing hands in a cir-cle through all lands. So-
truth and jus-tice, eq-ui-ty, all cre-a-tion whole and free.

Coda

shin-ing bright. Shin - ing bright! (yeah!)

49 Sophia Wisdom Comes to All

Proverbs 3:17; John 8:32

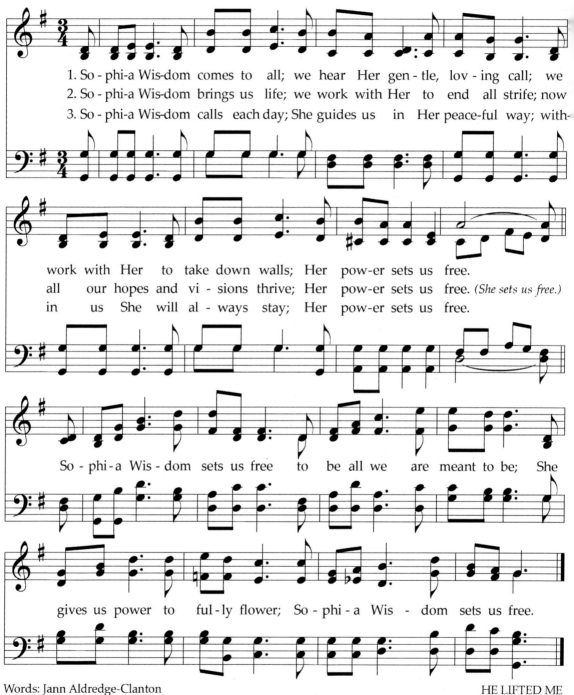

1. So-phi-a Wis-dom comes to all; we hear Her gen-tle, lov-ing call; we
2. So-phi-a Wis-dom brings us life; we work with Her to end all strife; now
3. So-phi-a Wis-dom calls each day; She guides us in Her peace-ful way; with-

work with Her to take down walls; Her pow-er sets us free.
all our hopes and vi-sions thrive; Her pow-er sets us free. *(She sets us free.)*
in us She will al-ways stay; Her pow-er sets us free.

So-phi-a Wis-dom sets us free to be all we are meant to be; She

gives us power to ful-ly flower; So-phi-a Wis-dom sets us free.

Words: Jann Aldredge-Clanton
Music: Charles H. Gabriel
Words © 2015 Jann Aldredge-Clanton.

HE LIFTED ME
8.8.8.6 with refrain

Sophia Wisdom Comes to Earth

50

Proverbs 3:17; Ephesians 6:14-15

1. So - phi - a Wis - dom comes to earth to teach us how to
2. Though all a - round the world we hear loud voic - es raised in
3. When un - just pow - ers seize con - trol, we rise up, we re -
4. So - phi - a Wis - dom calls us now to act for peace on

live; Her peace - ful paths show us the way to
fear, So - phi - a Wis - dom comes to bring Her
sist; So - phi - a Wis - dom gives us grace and
earth; with grat - i - tude we lift our song to

love and to for - give, to love and to for - give.
hope - ful mes - sage near, Her hope - ful mes - sage near.
cour - age to per - sist, and cour - age to per - sist.
cel - e - brate Her birth, to cel - e - brate Her birth.

Words: Jann Aldredge-Clanton
Music: Weyman's *Melodia Sacra*, 1815; arr. from George Frideric Handel
Words © 2017 Jann Aldredge-Clanton.

CHRISTMAS
8.6.8.6 (CM)

51 Sophia Wisdom Is Calling

Proverbs 1:20-23; 1 Corinthians 1:24

1. So - phi - a Wis-dom is call - ing; Her voice reach-es out to all;
2. So - phi - a Wis-dom em - brac - es each gen - der and ev - ery race;
3. So - phi - a Wis-dom in - spires us to work for e - qual - i - ty;

Her lov - ing mes - sage em - powers us to take down di - vid - ing walls.
She draws all peo - ple to - geth - er in Her all - in - clu - sive grace.
She gives us cour - age to rise up with ac - tion to set all free.

How wel - com - ing, how nur - tur - ing is So - phi - a's ten - der care;

how wel - com - ing, how nur - tur - ing is Her love for all to share.

Words: Jann Aldredge-Clanton
Music: Charles H. Gabriel
Words © 2017 Jann Aldredge-Clanton.

MY SAVIOR'S LOVE
8.7.8.7 with refrain

The Long-Ignored Disciples

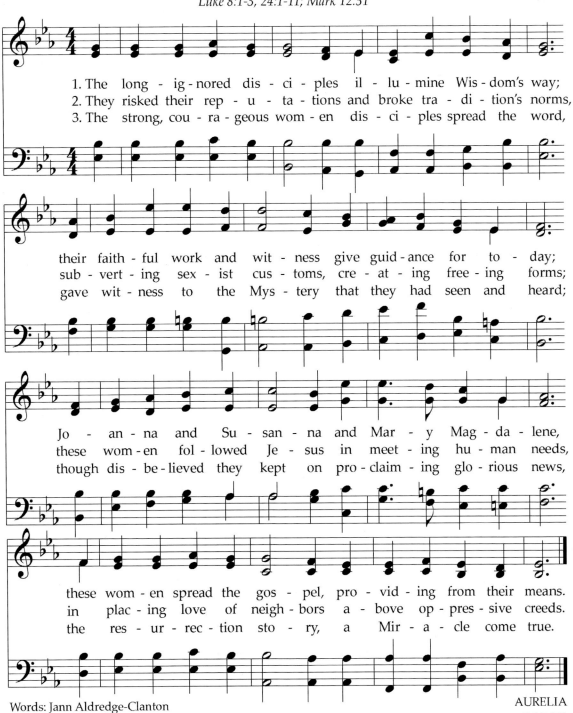

52

Luke 8:1-3, 24:1-11; Mark 12:31

1. The long-ignored disciples illumine Wisdom's way;
2. They risked their reputations and broke tradition's norms,
3. The strong, courageous women disciples spread the word,

their faithful work and witness give guidance for today;
subverting sexist customs, creating freeing forms;
gave witness to the Mystery that they had seen and heard;

Joanna and Susanna and Mary Magdalene,
these women followed Jesus in meeting human needs,
though disbelieved they kept on proclaiming glorious news,

these women spread the gospel, providing from their means.
in placing love of neighbors above oppressive creeds.
the resurrection story, a Miracle come true.

Words: Jann Aldredge-Clanton
Music: Samuel Sebastian Wesley
Words © 2017 Jann Aldredge-Clanton.

AURELIA
7.6.7.6 D

53 The Prophet Anna Sees New Life

Luke 2:36-38

1. The proph-et An - na sees new life at last this bless-ed morn,
2. The proph-et An - na prays for years with fast-ing day and night;
3. Though sel - dom is her sto - ry told, she ris-es to be heard;
4. The proph-et An - na speaks to - day; her mes-sage still a - bides;

the Prom-ised One to end the strife; So - phi - a - Christ is born;
she o - ver-comes her doubts and fears to keep her vi - sion bright,
the proph-et An - na, wise and bold, still preach-es Wis-dom - Word,
she shows us all the heal - ing Way, So - phi - a - Christ, our Guide,

So - phi - a - Christ is born; So - phi - a - Christ is born,
to keep her vi - sion bright, to keep her vi - sion bright;
still preach-es Wis - dom - Word, still preach-es Wis - dom-Word;
So - phi - a - Christ, our Guide, So - phi - a - Christ, our Guide;

the Prom-ised One to end the strife; So - phi - a - Christ is born.
she o - ver-comes her doubts and fears to keep her vi - sion bright.
the proph-et An - na, wise and bold, still preach-es Wis - dom - Word.
she shows us all the heal - ing Way, So - phi - a - Christ, our Guide.

Words: Jann Aldredge-Clanton
Music: Ananias Davisson's *Kentucky Harmony*, 2nd ed., 1817
Words © 2017 Jann Aldredge-Clanton.

PISGAH
8.6.8.6.6.6.8.6

The Spirit Dwells Within Us All

54

Galatians 5:22

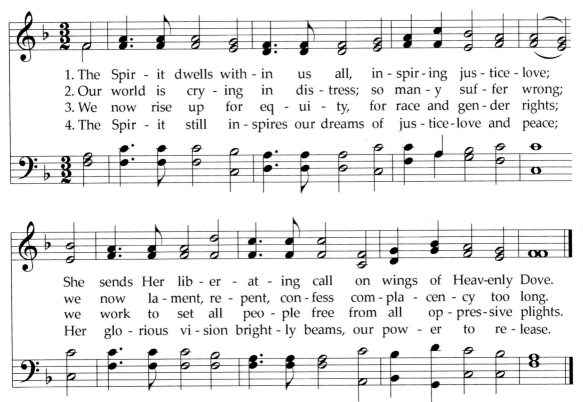

1. The Spir - it dwells with - in us all, in - spir - ing jus - tice - love;
2. Our world is cry - ing in dis - tress; so man - y suf - fer wrong;
3. We now rise up for eq - ui - ty, for race and gen - der rights;
4. The Spir - it still in - spires our dreams of jus - tice - love and peace;

She sends Her lib - er - at - ing call on wings of Heav-enly Dove.
we now la - ment, re - pent, con - fess com - pla - cen - cy too long.
we work to set all peo - ple free from all op - pres-sive plights.
Her glo - rious vi - sion bright - ly beams, our pow - er to re - lease.

Words: Jann Aldredge-Clanton
Music: Thomas Augustine Arne
Words © 2017 Jann Aldredge-Clanton.

ARLINGTON
8.6.8.6 (CM)

55 "Time's Up," We Shout!

Amos 5:21-24; John 8:32

1. We are tired of a-buse, ex-ploi-ta-tion, mis-use, so we join in the
2. There are those who ha-rass with their ac-tions so crass; they as-sault with their
3. As our sto-ries in-crease, gen-der vio-lence will cease, and at last we will

move-ment "Me Too"; break-ing si-lence, we shout and to-geth-er speak
words and their deeds; now the wom-en will rise with the truth un-dis-
have eq-ui-ty; now the time is at hand for a change in each

out, claim-ing voic-es with pow-er a-new.
guised, rais-ing voic-es that all will now heed.
land, for the truth will set ev-ery-one free.

"Time's Up," we shout! We will join to speak out. "We de-

mand gen-der jus-tice, for the Time's Up," we shout.

Words: Jann Aldredge-Clanton
Music: Daniel B. Towner
Words © 2018 Jann Aldredge-Clanton.

TRUST AND OBEY
6.6.9 D with refrain

We All Dream of Peace and Justice   56

Romans 15:13

1. We all dream of peace and jus - tice; we long to
2. When our hearts grow weak and wea - ry, and all our
3. Now we feel the power with - in us, and we can

keep our dream a - live. Come, join with our Sis - ter - Broth - er
striv - ing seems in vain, we call on our Sis - ter - Broth - er
make the world a - new. We join with our Sis - ter - Broth - er

Spir - it; cre - ate a world where all can thrive.
Spir - it, and we find hope to ease the pain.
Spir - it, giv - ing the world a wid - er view.

Words: Jann Aldredge-Clanton
Music: American folk hymn

LONESOME VALLEY
8.8.10.8

Words © 2016 Jann Aldredge-Clanton.

57   We All Rise Up for Human Rights

1. We all rise up for hu-man rights for all in ev-ery na-tion; we
2. We all rise up for wom-en's rights for e-qual pay and pow-er, for
3. We all rise up for e-qual rights for ev-ery race and gen-der, for
4. We all rise up for work-ers' rights, fair ben-e-fits and wag-es, for

all re-flect di-vin-i-ty through-out the whole cre-a-tion.
wom-en's rights are hu-man rights for all to ful-ly flow-er.
e-qual rights are hu-man rights that we will not sur-ren-der.
work-ers' rights are hu-man rights for all through-out the ag-es.

March-ing on for hu-man rights, march-ing on to-geth-er,

we will join the jus-tice march in an-y kind of weath-er.

Words: Jann Aldredge-Clanton
Music: Traditional folk tune
Words © 2017 Jann Aldredge-Clanton.

FATH'R AND I WENT DOWN TO CAMP
8.7.8.7 with refrain

We Praise Sacred Darkness, Creator of All 58

Psalm 139:12; Isaiah 45:3; Proverbs 3:17; Mark 12:31

1. We praise Sa-cred Dark - ness, Cre - a - tor of all, con-
2. So man - y still suf - fer op - pres-sion each day. How
3. Re - claim Sa-cred Dark - ness to bring peace on earth; She

nect - ing us all through Her life - giv - ing call; the
long will in - jus - tice and vio - lence hold sway? We
gives us all pow - er, af - firm - ing our worth; the

Lu - mi - nous Dark - ness draws all in - to one, cre -
join in the move - ment to o - ver-come wrong, em -
Lu - mi - nous Dark - ness in - spires heal - ing dreams, re -

at - ing a world where Her jus - tice is done.
brac - ing all peo - ple so love will grow strong.
veal - ing Her treas - ures of mir - a - cle streams.

Words: Jann Aldredge-Clanton
Music: A. J. Gordon
Words © 2017 Jann Aldredge-Clanton.

GORDON
11.11.11.11

59 We Are a People on a Journey

Based on the Covenant of Myers Park Baptist Church, Charlotte, NC

1. We are a peo-ple on a jour-ney, o-pen to all and
2. O - pen to all new light be-fore us, guid-ing be-yond what
3. When on our jour-ney we en-coun-ter stran-gers ig-nored or
4. Come, lift your voice in cel - e - bra-tion; join the pro - ces - sion

closed to none, led by the love we've known to-geth - er,
we can see, trust-ing a faith in - formed by rea - son,
friends in need, na - ture ne - glect-ed, life en - dan-gered,
through the world: grow-ing, ex - plor-ing, march - ing, sing-ing,

warm - ly em - brac - ing ev - ery - one. On the path of
chal - lenged with - in com - mu - ni - ty, we'll ex - plore vast
vic - tims op - pressed by power and greed, we will take a
ban - ners of love for all un - furled! Liv - ing just - ly,

Words and Music: Larry E. Schultz
Words and Music © 2018 Larry E. Schultz.

FOREVER FORWARD
Irregular

faith pro - gress - ing, firm - ly stead - fast, bold - ly free,
ways of wis - dom, search for mean - ing all a - round
stand for jus - tice; we will join our hands for peace;
serv - ing kind - ly, walk - ing hum - bly through our days,

we will move for - ev - er for - ward grow - ing in di -
as we move for - ev - er for - ward seek - ing truth wher -
then we'll move for - ev - er for - ward bear - ing hope that
let us move for - ev - er for - ward rais - ing songs of

1, 2, 3.   4.

ver - si - ty, grow - ing in di - ver - si - ty.
ev - er found, seek - ing truth wher - ev - er found.
fear may cease, bear - ing hope that fear may cease.
joy and praise, rais - ing songs of joy and   praise!

60 We Lift Our Voice and Celebrate*

Luke 4:18; Philippians 1:3-4

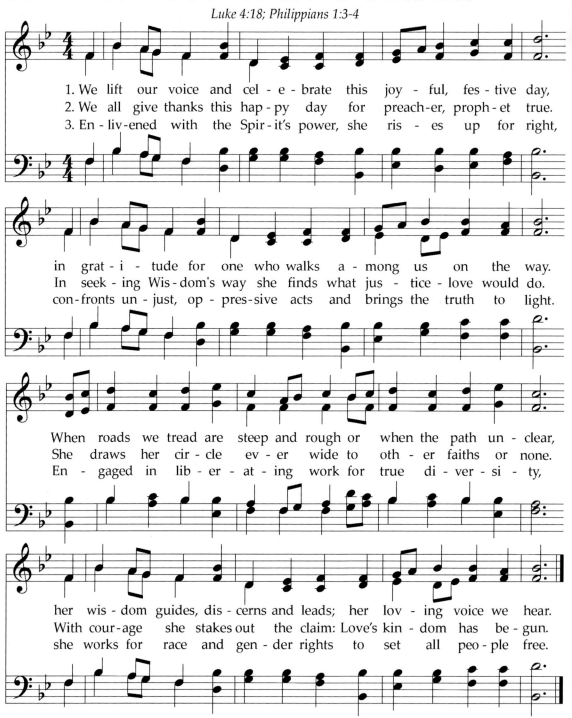

1. We lift our voice and cel-e-brate this joy-ful, fes-tive day,
2. We all give thanks this hap-py day for preach-er, proph-et true.
3. En-liv-ened with the Spir-it's power, she ris-es up for right,

in grat-i-tude for one who walks a-mong us on the way.
In seek-ing Wis-dom's way she finds what jus-tice-love would do.
con-fronts un-just, op-pres-sive acts and brings the truth to light.

When roads we tread are steep and rough or when the path un-clear,
She draws her cir-cle ev-er wide to oth-er faiths or none.
En-gaged in lib-er-at-ing work for true di-ver-si-ty,

her wis-dom guides, dis-cerns and leads; her lov-ing voice we hear.
With cour-age she stakes out the claim: Love's kin-dom has be-gun.
she works for race and gen-der rights to set all peo-ple free.

Words: Larry E. Schultz (St. 1), Patricia V. Long (St. 2), Jann Aldredge-Clanton (St. 3)
Music: *Wittenberg Gesangbuch*, 1784
Words © 2017 Larry E. Schultz, Patricia V. Long & Jann Aldredge-Clanton.

ELLACOMBE
8.6.8.6 D (CMD)
*sung in celebration of an individual

We Lift Our Voice and Celebrate   60a

Luke 4:18; Philippians 1:3-4

1. We lift our voice and cel - e - brate this joy - ful, fes - tive day,
2. We all give thanks this hap - py day for preach-ers, proph-ets true.
3. En - liv-ened with the Spir - it's power, they all rise up for right,

in grat - i - tude for those who walk a - mong us on the way.
In seek - ing Wis - dom's way they find what jus - tice - love would do.
con - front un - just, op - pres-sive acts and bring the truth to light.

When roads we tread are steep and rough or when the path un - clear,
They draw their cir - cles ev - er wide to oth - er faiths or none.
En - gaged in lib - er - at - ing work for true di - ver - si - ty,

their wis - dom guides, dis - cerns and leads; their lov - ing voice we hear.
With cour - age they stake out the claim: Love's kin - dom has be - gun.
they work for race and gen - der rights to set all peo - ple free.

Words: Larry E. Schultz (St. 1), Patricia V. Long (St. 2), Jann Aldredge-Clanton (St. 3)
Music: *Wittenberg Gesangbuch*, 1784

ELLACOMBE
8.6.8.6 D (CMD)

61   We Sing of Faithful Women

Matthew 5:14; Luke 4:18-19; John 14:6; 1 Corinthians 1:24; 2 Timothy 1:7

1. We sing of faith-ful wom-en who show the gos-pel Way;
2. We cel-e-brate the wom-en who take down ev-ery wall,
3. Or-dained by Christ-So-phi-a, in-spired by Love Di-vine,
4. We sing of faith-ful wom-en, bold proph-ets through the years;

through lov-ing words and ac-tions, they fol-low Truth each day.
who give their gra-cious wel-come to an-y-one and all.
the faith-ful wom-en wit-ness to make their vi-sions shine.
the Spir-it gives them pow-er to o-ver-come all fears.

They la-bor long with cour-age to set the cap-tives free;
No creed or church tra-di-tion can lim-it wom-en's gifts;
Em-pow-ered by the Spir-it for mis-sions ev-ery-where,
Their work of lib-er-a-tion brings new cre-a-tion's birth,

pro-claim-ing peace and whole-ness, they build com-mu-ni-ty.
they teach and preach with pas-sion, all peo-ple to up-lift.
they bring the Word of Good News for ev-ery-one to share.
trans-form-ing world-wide church-es, de-light-ing heaven and earth.

Words: Jann Aldredge-Clanton
Music: Larry E. Schultz
EVA
7.6.7.6 D

*Cue-sized notes for final stanza

We Sing of Faithful Women

61a

Matthew 5:14; Luke 4:18-19; John 14:6; 1 Corinthians 1:24; 2 Timothy 1:7

1. We sing of faith-ful wom-en who show the gos-pel Way;
2. We cel-e-brate the wom-en who take down ev-ery wall,
3. Or-dained by Christ-So-phi-a, in-spired by Love Di-vine,
4. We sing of faith-ful wom-en, bold proph-ets through the years;

through lov-ing words and ac-tions, they fol-low Truth each day.
who give their gra-cious wel-come to an-y-one and all.
the faith-ful wom-en wit-ness to make their vi-sions shine.
the Spir-it gives them pow-er to o-ver-come all fears.

They la-bor long with cour-age to set the cap-tives free;
No creed or church tra-di-tion can lim-it wom-en's gifts;
Em-pow-ered by the Spir-it for mis-sions ev-ery-where,
Their work of lib-er-a-tion brings new cre-a-tion's birth,

pro-claim-ing peace and whole-ness, they build com-mu-ni-ty.
they teach and preach with pas-sion, all peo-ple to up-lift.
they bring the Word of Good News for ev-ery-one to share.
trans-form-ing world-wide church-es, de-light-ing heaven and earth.

Words: Jann Aldredge-Clanton
Music: *Wittenberg Gesangbuch*, 1784
Words © 2017 Jann Aldredge-Clanton.

ELLACOMBE
7.6.7.6 D

62

We Will All Resist

Proverbs 28:4; 1 Peter 5:8-9

Refrain

We will rise up; we will all re-sist; we will rise up; we will all re-sist, for we will rise up strong-er all to-geth - er; we will all re - sist.

Fine

Stanzas selected as appropriate (additional stanzas on opposite page)

E - qual rights for wom - en will not be de-nied; e - qual rights for wom - en
Jus - tice for all rac - es will not be de-nied; jus - tice for all rac - es
Jus - tice for all gen - ders will not be de-nied; jus - tice for all gen - ders

D.C. al Fine

will not be de-nied, for we will rise up strong-er all to-geth-er; we will all re - sist.
will not be de-nied, for we will rise up strong-er all to-geth-er; we will all re - sist.
will not be de-nied, for we will rise up strong-er all to-geth-er; we will all re - sist.

Words: Jann Aldredge-Clanton
Music: African-American spiritual
Words © 2017 Jann Aldredge-Clanton.

I SHALL NOT BE MOVED
Irregular

We Will All Resist
Additional Stanzas

Immigrants will not be ever turned away;
immigrants will not be ever turned away,
for we will rise up stronger all together;
we will all resist.

Rights of workers will not ever be denied;
rights of workers will not ever be denied,
for we will rise up stronger all together;
we will all resist.

Care of Earth will never ever be denied;
care of Earth will never ever be denied,
for we will rise up stronger all together;
we will all resist.

Public schools will not be ever undermined;
public schools will not be ever undermined,
for we will rise up stronger all together;
we will all resist.

Healthcare rights will never ever be denied;
healthcare rights will never ever be denied,
for we will rise up stronger all together;
we will all resist.

Travel bans will never ever be the law;
travel bans will never ever be the law,
for we will rise up stronger all together;
we will all resist.

Women's voices will not ever be shut down;
women's voices will not ever be shut down,
for we will rise up stronger all together;
we will all resist.

Human rights will never ever be denied;
human rights will never ever be denied,
for we will rise up stronger all together;
we will all resist.

63　We Work for Jobs with Justice Now

Exodus 6:2-8

1. We work for jobs with jus-tice now, for true e-qual-i-ty;
2. We join to-geth-er, claim-ing pow-er; as work-ers we u-nite;
3. We work to stop in-jus-tice now, to end op-pres-sive ways;
4. Come, Sis-ter-Broth-er Spir-it, come and heal our wound-ed past;

come, Sis-ter-Broth-er Spir-it, come and help us all be free.
come, Sis-ter-Broth-er Spir-it, come, re-store our hu-man rights.
come, Sis-ter-Broth-er Spir-it, come and guide to bet-ter days.
to-geth-er we will all rise up so all are free at last.

We are claim-ing the prom-ised land; we are claim-ing the prom-ised land;

come, sis-ters, broth-ers, hand in hand; we are claim-ing the prom-ised land.

Words: Jann Aldredge-Clanton
Music: Matilda T. Durham; W. Walker's *Southern Harmony*, 1835
Words © 2014 Jann Aldredge-Clanton.

PROMISED LAND
8.6.8.6 (CM) with refrain

We're Gonna Join in the Movement   64

We're gon-na join   in the move-ment for   peace;   we're gon-na
(march, sing, shout)

join   in   the move-ment for   peace;   we're gon-na
(march, sing, shout)

join   in   the move-ment   for   peace,   and   de -
(march, sing, shout)

mand   for   jus-tice   to   in - crease!

Words: Jann Aldredge-Clanton
Music: African-American spiritual; arr. Larry E. Schultz

I'M GONNA SING WHEN THE SPIRIT SAYS SING
Irregular

65 When People Follow Wisdom's Way

Proverbs 3:17-18; John 8:32

1. When peo-ple fol-low Wis-dom's way,
2. When wom-en have e-qual-i-ty,
3. When ra-cial jus-tice comes on earth, She will set us free;
4. When work-ers' rights be-come the norm,
5. When peo-ple join in Wis-dom's plan,

then truth will tri-umph day by day;
then all can be all we can be;
then all will know each oth-er's worth; She will set us free.
then all join hands to bring re-form;
then peace will come to ev-ery land;

Fol-low Wis-dom; claim Her trans-form-ing pow-er;

tell all peo-ple: She will set us free.

Words: Jann Aldredge-Clanton
Music: African-American spiritual
Words © 2017 Jann Aldredge-Clanton.

GO DOWN MOSES
Irregular

When the Workers All Unite

66

Words: Jann Aldredge-Clanton
Music: African-American spiritual; arr. Larry E. Schultz
Words © 2015 Jann Aldredge-Clanton; Music arr. © 2018 Larry E. Schultz.

WHEN THE SAINTS
8.8.10.7

67 Wisdom Shows Us Peaceful Pathways

Proverbs 3:17-18

1. Wis - dom shows us peace - ful path - ways, giv - ing hope to keep a - live; joined with Her we go on mis - sion, help - ing all cre - a - tion thrive.
2. Wis - dom guides our work of jus - tice, send - ing pow - er to per - sist; when we face op - pres - sive sys - tems, She gives cour - age to re - sist.
3. Wis - dom helps us on our jour - ney, shar - ing bur - dens that we bear; joined with Her to meet each chal - lenge, we can all be kind and fair.
4. Wis - dom calls us now to rise up all to - geth - er for re - form; joined with Her in lov - ing ac - tion, we cre - ate a world trans - formed.

Words: Jann Aldredge-Clanton
Music: William H. Jude
Words © 2017 Jann Aldredge-Clanton.

GALILEE
8.7.8.7

NOTES ON THE SONGS

These songs are among those in this collection inspired by my participation in the Women's March on January 21, 2017, and in the social justice movement that has followed. Millions of people in the United States and around the world have marched and rallied for women's rights and connecting justice concerns. These songs focus on women's rights and intersecting justice issues such as racial justice, immigrant rights, LGBTQ rights, environmental justice, rights to healthcare, and rights to education.

2.   And Still We Rise

Equity for Women in the Church, which I co-chair with Rev. Sheila Sholes-Ross, is a national, ecumenical organization with the mission of facilitating equal representation of clergywomen as pastors of multi-cultural churches in order to transform church and society. "Calling in the Key of She," one of Equity's projects coordinated by Rev. Andrea Clark Chambers, provides programs to educate and empower congregations to become more open to women leaders. At one of these programs we sang "And Still We Rise." Inspired by Maya Angelou's poem "Still I Rise," this song connects long-ignored biblical women leaders to women today who rise up as religious leaders in spite of exclusion and discrimination.

4.   As We Come to the Table of Love

Rev. Dr. Nancy E. Petty, pastor of Pullen Memorial Baptist Church in Raleigh, North Carolina, and Rev. Larry E. Schultz, minister of music at this church, collaborated on the words and music to "As We Come to the Table of Love." It was included as a short song in *Earth Transformed with Music! Inclusive Songs for Worship* (Eakin Press, 2015), and is expanded in this collection to include stanzas. The phrase "ever embracing" in the second stanza is a self-description of Pullen prominently displayed in the church's recent sanctuary art installation. At Pullen and many other churches the act of communion in worship is one in which diverse people of all ages and beliefs may participate.

8.   **Come, Christ-Sophia, Come, We Pray**
9.   **Come, Gather Now in Circles**
24.   **Longing for Her Rebirth**
28.   **Our Hearts Cry Out in Longing**
43.   **Sing of Holy Wisdom**
47.   **Sophia, Holy Wisdom**
50.   **Sophia Wisdom Comes to Earth**

Inclusive lyrics to most of the well-known Christmas carol tunes are published in my first three hymn collections in collaboration with Larry E. Schultz. New Wineskins Feminist Ritual Community in Dallas, Ebenezer/ herchurch Lutheran in San Francisco, and other faith communities have requested additional inclusive Advent and Christmas carols. My gratitude goes to these communities for encouraging me to write these new songs to other traditional carol tunes. These Advent and Christmas carols in this collection focus on the biblical image of Wisdom (*Sophia* in the Greek language of the Christian Scriptures), and express longing for Her to be born again to bring peace and justice to our world. The name "Christ-Sophia," in one of these carols, comes from the connection between Christ and Wisdom in the Bible and in Christian history. My book *In Search of the Christ-Sophia: An Inclusive Christology for Liberating Christians* gives biblical, historical, and theological explanation of this connection.

The Dallas Workers' Rights Board inspired these songs. For many years I have served on the board of this organization, which brings faith and labor leaders together in support of workers' rights. Collaborating with Workers Defense Project and Jobs with Justice, the Dallas Workers' Rights Board advocates for fair wages, healthcare and other benefits, and safe working conditions. These songs can be used in workers' rights marches, rallies, and meetings.

26.   Mother Eve Chose Love of Knowledge

The inspiration for this song came from *If Eve Only Knew: Freeing Yourself from Biblical Womanhood & Becoming All God Means for You to Be*, by Dr. Kendra Weddle and Dr. Melanie Springer Mock. Though many commentators down through the centuries have demeaned Eve as responsible for all the sin in the world, Kendra and Melanie give a more accurate interpretation of Eve as a wise woman who embraced the fullness of life. Drawing from this positive interpretation, this song reclaims Eve's "life-affirming power."

27.   Now the Spirit Comes

At an Equity for Women in the Church conference, people from diverse cultures sang "Blessed Quietness" with great enthusiasm. I felt inspired to write new lyrics to this tune I love. "Now the Spirit Comes" premiered at an ecumenical conference titled "Unauthorized: Nevertheless, She Preached," featuring powerful women preachers who have faced obstacles and met challenges in patriarchal denominations. Organized by Rev. Kyndall Rothaus and Rev. Natalie Webb, it was a dynamic event that fully acknowledged and celebrated women's voices, our reality, our calling, our preaching, and our songwriting.

29.   Prathia Hall Spoke Up

The inspiration for this song came from Rev. Dr. Courtney Pace's work on Rev. Dr. Prathia Hall. Courtney, a church history professor at Memphis Theological Seminary, also serves on the board of Equity for Women in the Church. Prathia, a courageous civil rights movement leader and womanist theologian, preached with such power that Dr. Martin Luther King Jr. once remarked, "Prathia Hall is one platform speaker I prefer not to follow." Courtney writes that Prathia "empowered people to realize their giftedness and calling in spite of obstacles; her faith inspired others to find their own."

30.   Queen Esther Saved Her People

The story of Esther and current events inspired the 2018 Christian Feminism Today Gathering theme: "Standing Up, Speaking Up In Such a Time as This" (Esther 4:14). This theme describes the social justice work of Evan-gelical & Ecumenical Women's Caucus–Christian Feminism Today, needed now more than ever. I wrote this song for the Gathering based on this theme and the interpretation of Esther by Princess O'Nika Auguste in her article "Was Esther a Post-Colonial Feminist?" in *Christian Feminism Today*.

31.   Radiant Mother
35.   Roses & Birds

Katie Ketchum, lead musician at Ebenezer/herchurch Lutheran in San Francisco, created the lyrics and music for these songs. When participating in herchurch liturgies, I have appreciated Katie's gifts as a singer, songwriter, pianist, and music director. At an annual fall festival, Katie sang "Roses & Birds" and gave a recording of this beautiful song to all who attended the performance. At the celebration of Pastor Stacy Boorn's 30 years of ministry, Katie led us in singing "Roses & Birds," based on the miracle of Our Lady of Guadalupe's appearing to Juan Diego and bringing roses and birds in the midst of winter. "Radiant Mother," another of Katie's lovely songs, is inspired by many Aramaic versions of Matthew 6:9-13 and Luke 11:2-4. My gratitude goes to Katie for contributing these songs to this collection.

37.   Sacred Spark of Life and Beauty

Ebenezer/herchurch Lutheran commissioned this song for a liturgy celebrating Brigid of Kildare's Feast Day. Brigid is an important Celtic Goddess and one of Ireland's patron saints. Brigid is the Goddess of fertility, spring, healing, poetry, music, and smithcraft. St. Brigid, an early

Christian nun and abbess, is associated with perpetual, sacred flames. Both Goddess Brigid and St. Brigid are associated with holy wells. Rev. Colette Numajiri, a co-leader of New Wineskins Feminist Ritual Community in Dallas, writes in her "Free Sophia" blog that Brigid is "Goddess of fire and light, patron of poets, smiths, and healers."

40. She Will Rise

Rev. Stacy Boorn, pastor of Ebenezer/herchurch Lutheran, wrote the words for this song, and Katie Ketchum wrote the music. "She Will Rise" was the theme song for herchurch's 2017 fall festival with the same title. The festival focused on social, political, environmental, and spiritual activism and creativity to promote partnership paradigms and paths for reclaiming justice. Included was a panel discussion to empower creative persistence and resistance, based on the timely theme, "She Will Rise!" I am grateful to Pastor Stacy and Katie for contributing this wonderful song to this collection.

44. Sister Hildegard Shows the Way

St. Hildegard's Community in Austin, Texas, provides a prophetic witness for social justice, peace, and care of creation. I wrote this song in celebration of the 20th anniversary of St. Hildegard's Community and in gratitude for this radically inclusive community and for Rev. Judith Liro, priest of St. Hildegard's. Judith, also a board member of Equity for Women in the Church, contributed her inspiring story to my books *Changing Church: Stories of Liberating Ministers* and *She Lives! Sophia Wisdom Works in the World*. This song refers to Hildegard's belief in the "greening power" of love, which St. Hildegard's Community embodies to transform individuals, the church, and the world. Also, the song alludes to Hildegard's work as visionary, healer, composer, religious leader, and reformer.

46. Sophia Friend

Rev. Brian Burton, president & CEO of Three Square Food Bank in Southern Nevada, and I collaborated on "Sophia Friend." Previously he served as executive director of the Wilkinson Center and minister to adults at Wilshire Baptist Church in Dallas. Brian's abundant gifts have also blessed New Wineskins Feminist Ritual Community. At a time when we were both in need of healing, Brian showed me lyrics he had begun writing to one of his favorite hymn tunes, SWEET HOUR, and asked me to join him in creating this song.

48.   Sophia, Waiting for Your Light

Katie Ketchum, lead musician at Ebenezer/herchurch Lutheran in San Francisco, created lyrics and contributed to the music arrangement for the refrain of this song, and I wrote the words for the stanzas. It was a joy to sing Katie's refrain at the celebration of Pastor Stacy Boorn's 30 years of ministry, and I was delighted when Katie asked me to write lyrics for the stanzas. Larry E. Schultz wrote alternate refrain lyrics with *Ruah* ("Spirit") so that this song can be sung for Pentecost as well as for Advent. Larry also contributed to the lively new arrangement of the tune WONDERFUL CHILD.

55.   "Time's Up," We Shout!

The "Me Too" movement, created in 2007 by Tarana Burke, gained momentum on social media in the fall of 2017, demonstrating the prevalence of sexual harassment and assault women suffer. In January of 2018 hundreds of Hollywood celebrities launched the "Time's Up" movement as the next step to the "Me Too" movement. These movements stirred me to write the song "'Time's Up,' We Shout!" The "Time's Up" movement calls for immediate change for women of all classes and races in all occupations. "Time's Up" has formed a legal defense fund to help women report sexual harrassment or assault. Also, this movement creates legislation that better penalizes sexual misconduct and advocates for gender equity in all industries. At the second Women's March on January 20, 2018, "Me Too" and "Time's Up" signs were on display around the world.

58.   We Praise Sacred Darkness, Creator of All

The inspiration for this song came from a sermon by Rev. Scott Shirley, pastor of Church in the Cliff in Dallas. In the sermon Scott stirred my imagination with the beautiful phrase "luminous darkness," from Gregory of Nyssa's *Life of Moses*. Gregory, a fourth century bishop and theologian, wrote that Moses met the Divine in the "luminous darkness." Scott explained that this "confounding language is the hallmark of Christian apophatic mystics, designed to break down the intellect and the senses," and that "the Gospel of John uses similar techniques to draw us into relationship" with Divine Mystery.

This song also continues my reclaiming of darkness as a positive image in worship to emphasize the sacred value of people of color. Through references to "Holy Darkness" and "Sacred Darkness" in my songs, I seek to change the traditional symbolism of light as positive and darkness as negative. "Luminous Darkness" and "Sacred Darkness" in this song are metaphors for Divine Mystery, drawing "all into one" to create a world of justice and peace.

59. We Are a People on a Journey

Myers Park Baptist Church in Charlotte, North Carolina, commissioned Larry E. Schultz to write the words and music for this hymn in celebration of the congregation's 75th anniversary. The history, worship, and ministry of Myers Park Baptist Church inspired "We Are a People on a Journey." Text and tune combine to express a vibrant proclamation of the church's identity, incorporating a "journey" metaphor as expressed in the congregation's covenant. Each stanza includes the 75th anniversary theme, "Forever Forward," as the hymn sings of "progressing," "exploring" and "processing" on the path of faith—halting only to "take a stand for justice." Larry created the tune, FOREVER FORWARD, with a processional feel to coordinate with the text's "journey" theme.

60, 60a. We Lift Our Voice and Celebrate

This hymn celebrates Rev. Dr. Nancy E. Petty on the occasion of her 25th anniversary in ministry with Pullen Memorial Baptist Church in Raleigh, North Carolina. Since 2010 she has served as senior pastor of Pullen. Previously she served as minister of education, associate pastor, and co-pastor. Rev. Larry E. Schultz, Pullen's minister of music, invited Pullen member Patricia V. Long and me to collaborate with him on the lyrics of "We Lift Our Voice and Celebrate." Larry wrote the first stanza to lift up Nancy's gifts as pastor, Pat wrote the second stanza in gratitude for Nancy's gifts as proclaimer, and I wrote the third stanza in celebration of her gifts as social activist. This hymn can be sung in celebration of other individuals.

Another version of this hymn (60a) can be sung to celebrate groups of people.

61, 61a. We Sing of Faithful Women

This hymn is dedicated in loving memory to my mother, Eva Louise Hickerson Aldredge Henley. "We Sing of Faithful Women" celebrates her ministries as teacher, preacher, missionary, and prophet. For 82 years she taught Sunday school and provided a variety of ministries to the members of her classes. The second stanza of this hymn alludes to a class she taught in San Angelo, Texas, for 35 years, aptly named "Any and All"; she not only welcomed all who came but invited anyone she met. Her class members have been of five races and of various ages, genders, and economic backgrounds—many who don't feel comfortable in other Sunday school classes and churches. In addition, she ministered to students for 25 years in her position as a high school English teacher. My mother included a diversity of people in her ministry as pastor's wife in four churches. Like my father, she had a seminary degree and abundant pastoral gifts. Her gregarious personality, dynamic speaking voice, and exceptional leadership skills made her every bit as qualified as my father to pastor a church. But she served churches as an unpaid, untitled outreach worker, events organizer, educator, and development officer. The second stanza also references her frequent comments about her preference for pastors who "preach with passion" and celebrates her preaching and teaching "with passion," undeterred by church traditions that try to limit women's gifts. The third stanza reflects my belief that in spite of suffering discrimination that bars women from ordination, she was "ordained by Christ-Sophia, inspired by Love Divine." This stanza also lifts up her mission work in her community and around the world. She co-founded a missions organization, led mission trips to eight countries, and raised money for missions around the world. The last stanza lifts up her courageous work as prophet, for many years advocating for women's ordination and for full gender equity. The hymn concludes on a note of rejoicing in the transformation that continues through her liberating ministry and that of other faithful women.

My gratitude goes to Larry E. Schultz for honoring my mother by composing a beautiful new tune for this hymn and naming the tune EVA. This flowing and majestic tune enhances the celebration of bold, faithful women whose ministry transforms churches around the world.

TOPICAL INDEX OF SONGS

ADVENT

CARE OF CREATION (see also Earth Day)

CHRISTMAS

DIVINE IMAGES

110

Wisdom-Word
Word

EARTH DAY (see also Care of Creation)

MARCHES AND RALLIES

MISSION

NEW LIFE

PEACE

PENTECOST

POWER FOR SOCIAL ACTION

RENEWAL

RESURRECTION

SOCIAL JUSTICE

UNITY AND DIVERSITY

VISION

WOMEN LEADERS IN HISTORY

WOMEN LEADERS IN SCRIPTURE

INDEX OF SCRIPTURE REFERENCES

121

INDEX OF COMPOSERS, AUTHORS, AND SOURCES

ALPHABETICAL INDEX OF TUNES

METRICAL INDEX OF TUNES

INDEX OF TITLES